Explorations

An Anthology of British and World Literature

Volume D

Book Staff & Contributors

John Holdren *Senior Vice President for Content and Curriculum*
Beth Zemble *Director, Alternative Learning Strategies; Director, Language Arts*
Cynthia Guidici *Content Specialist*
Marianne Murphy *Content Specialist*
Tim Mansfield *Writer*
Suzanne Montazer *Senior Art Director*
David Reinhold *Print Designer*
Kim Barcas *Cover Designer*
Stephanie Shaw *Illustrator*
Jean Stringer *Rights Specialist*
Annette Scarpitta *Media Editor*
Joel Storer *Text Editor*
Elia Ben-Ari *Text Editor*
Mary Beck Desmond *Text Editor*
Sarah Allard *Project Manager*

Bror Saxberg *Chief Learning Officer*
John Holdren *Senior Vice President for Content and Curriculum*
Maria Szalay *Senior Vice President for Product Development*
David Pelizzari *Senior Director, Product Development*
Kim Barcas *Creative Director*
Jeff Burridge *Managing Editor*
Sally Russell *Senior Manager, Media*
Chris Frescholtz *Senior Project Manager, High School*
Corey Maender *Director, Program Management*
Lisa Dimaio Iekel *Production Manager*
John G. Agnone *Director of Publications*

Cover: London houses of Parliament and Big Ben from River Thames. ©
XtravaganT/Fotolia; Stone bridge and mountains. © John Short/Jupiterimages

About K12 Inc.

K12 Inc., a technology-based education company, is the nation's leading provider of proprietary curriculum and online education programs to students in grades K–12. K12 provides its curriculum and academic services to online schools, traditional classrooms, blended school programs, and directly to families. K12 Inc. also operates the K12 International Academy, an accredited, diploma-granting online private school serving students worldwide. K12's mission is to provide any child the curriculum and tools to maximize success in life, regardless of geographic, financial, or demographic circumstances. K12 Inc. is accredited by CITA. More information can be found at www.K12.com.

ISBN: 1-60153-035-8   Printed in U.S.A.

Printed by Worzalla, Stevens Point, WI, USA, July 2012, LOT 072012

Contents

Stories of Heroes

Love and Beauty

THE NATURAL WORLD

SHERLOCK HOLMES MYSTERIES

CHALLENGES AND TURNING POINTS

Stories of Heroes

from MORTE D'ARTHUR

Sir Thomas Malory

Morte d'Arthur, which includes the stories of King Arthur and the Knights of the Round Table, is a collection of legends from the Middle Ages. These legends contain stories of Arthur's birth, his rise to the throne, and the adventures of the fellowship of knights who served him. The stories conclude with Arthur's death and the dissolution of the fellowship and kingdom. Sir Thomas Malory (1394–1471) translated these tales of chivalry, courage, honor, magic, and romance from the original French and wrote them in English prose.

ARTHUR BECOMES KING

On the day of his birth, Arthur was taken from his parents by the soothsayer Merlin, and placed with the family of Sir Ector for rearing. No one at the court knew where he was, nor was Sir Ector told of his young ward's noble parentage.

When Arthur was but two years old, his father, Uther Pendragon, died, as is told in the selection which follows. Then for many years the throne was open, and powerful nobles eyed it greedily.

And then King Uther fell sore sick, and for three days and nights he was speechless, so that all the barons turned to Merlin for counsel.

---

soothsayer: wizard
Merlin: a legendary wizard and a prominent figure in Arthurian legends
Sir Ector: an important figure in Arthurian legend who served as something of a
    foster father to Arthur after King Uther's death
rearing: raising
ward: one who is in the custody of another
Uther Pendragon: a legendary king of Britain and father of King Arthur
counsel: advice

"There is no remedy but God's will," said Merlin. "But let all the barons come before the King tomorrow morn, and God and I will make him speak."

On the morrow morn, Merlin and all the nobles came to the King.

"Sir," said Merlin, "shall your son Arthur be King of this realm after you?"

And Uther Pendragon turned to him and said in the hearing of all, "I give him God's blessing and mine, and bid him pray for my soul. But he will forfeit my blessing if he does not claim the crown which is rightly his." And so saying, he died.

Uther was buried as befits a king, and fair Igraine and the barons drank deep of sorrow.

Then stood the realm in great jeopardy for a long while, for every powerful lord made himself stronger, and many wished to be king. Then Merlin went to the Archbishop of Canterbury and counseled him to bid all the lords of the realm, and all gentlemen-at-arms, to come to London by Christmas upon pain of cursing. He argued that Jesus, who was born on that night to be King of Mankind, would of his mercy show by some miracle who was to be King of this realm.

The Archbishop followed his counsel, and ordered all the lords and gentlemen-at-arms to come to London by Christmas. And many of them confessed their sins and did penance, that their prayer might be the more acceptable unto God.

So in the greatest church of London (whether it was St. Paul's or not, the French book does not say), all the lords and knights were praying long before dawn. And when Matins and the first Mass were done, there was seen in the churchyard, near the high altar, a great stone, four square, seemingly of marble. In the middle of the stone was written in letters of gold:

Igraine: Arthur's mother

Archbishop of Canterbury: traditionally, the Archibishop of Canterbury is the
    highest-ranking religious official in Britain

gentlemen-at-arms: armed military officers

upon pain of cursing: under the threat of being excommunicated from the Church

the French book: the French book from which Malory takes these stories; a history
    of Britain written in verse by a twelfth-century poet from Normandy, France

Matins: morning prayers

3

WHOEVER PULLS THIS SWORD
OUT OF THE STONE IS BORN
TRUE KING OF ALL ENGLAND.

The people marveled; but the Archbishop said, "I command that you stay within the church and pray to God still. Let no man touch the sword until the High Mass be done."

When all the Masses were done, the lords went to view the stone and the sword. And when they had seen the writing, some— those that would be King—tried to remove the sword from the stone. But none could move either the sword or the stone.

"He that shall win the sword is not here," said the Archbishop. "But doubt not that God will make him known. Meanwhile, let us set ten knights of good fame as guards over the sword."

Orders were so given, and it was publicly announced that any man who wished might try to win the sword.

On New Year's Day the barons held jousts and a tourney for all the knights there, in order to keep together the knights and the commons, for the Archbishop trusted that God would soon make known him who would win the sword. And when the Mass was over, the barons rode to the field where the jousts and tourney were to be held.

So it happened that Sir Ector, who had much property around London, rode to the field also, and with him his son Sir Kay and young Arthur, his ward. As they rode toward the field, Sir Kay missed his sword, having left it at his father's lodging. He asked young Arthur to ride back for it.

"Gladly," said Arthur, and rode back with all speed. When he came to the house, he found that all the ladies had left to see the jousting, and he could not find the sword. He was angry, then, and said to himself, "I will ride to the churchyard, and take the sword that is stuck in the stone. My brother Sir Kay will not be without a sword today!"

When he came to the churchyard, he found no one there, for the guard had all gone to the jousting. So he took the sword by the

---

tourney: a contest between armored knights
Sir Kay: the son of Sir Ector and an eventual Knight of the Round Table; he is
    sometimes described as a half brother or a foster brother of Arthur

handle and easily pulled it out of the stone. He then rode on with the sword until he came to his brother Sir Kay, and gave the sword to him.

As soon as Sir Kay saw it, he knew that it was the Sword of the Stone. He rode up to his father and said, "Sir, see here the Sword of the Stone—which means that I must be King of this land."

When Sir Ector saw the sword, he turned back. When all three had come to the church, they dismounted and went inside. Then Sir Ector ordered Sir Kay to swear on the Gospels how he came by that sword.

"Sir," said Kay, "from my brother Arthur, who brought it to me."

"How got you the sword?" asked Sir Ector to Arthur.

Arthur answered, "Sir, when I came home for my brother's sword, I found no one there to give it to me. I did not want my brother Sir Kay to be without a sword, so I came here quickly and pulled this one out of the stone with no trouble."

"Were there any knights around the sword?" asked Sir Ector.

"No," said Arthur.

"Now," said Sir Ector to Arthur, "I know that you must be King of this land."

"I?" said Arthur. "For what cause?"

"Because God will have it so," said Sir Ector. "No man could have drawn out the sword but he that shall be true King of this land. Now let me see whether you can put the sword back in the stone as it was, and pull it out again."

"That is easy," said Arthur, and put it back in the stone. And Sir Ector tried to pull out the sword, and failed.

"Now you try," said he to Sir Kay. Sir Kay tried with all his might, but failed.

"Now shall you try," said Sir Ector to Arthur.

"Gladly," said Arthur, and pulled it out easily. At that, Sir Ector and Sir Kay knelt before him.

"But my own dear father and brother, why kneel to me?" said Arthur.

Sir Ector said, "No, no, my lord Arthur, it is not so. I am not your father, nor of your blood. But I know now that you are of higher blood than I thought before." And so he told Arthur the whole story—how he had been fostered, and at whose orders.

Arthur wept bitterly when he understood that Sir Ector was not his father.

"Sir," said Ector to Arthur, "I beg you be a good and gracious lord to me when you are King."

"I would be ungrateful otherwise," said Arthur, "for I owe no man in all the world as much as I owe you and your lady wife, who has cared for me as for her own. If ever I am King as you say, I shall grant whatever you may ask. God forbid that I should fail you."

Sir Ector said, "I ask but one thing of you—that you make my son, your foster brother, Seneschal of your lands."

Arthur answered, "That shall be done, and more. No other man shall have that office while he and I live."

Then they went to the Archbishop, and told him how the sword had been won, and by whom. On Twelfth Day all the barons came to try to take the sword, but none could pull it from the stone but Arthur. At this many of the lords were angry, and said that it was a great shame to them all and to the realm to be governed by a boy of no high blood born. So it was agreed that another trial should be made at Candlemas, when all the lords would come together again. Meanwhile, ten knights were appointed to guard the sword day and night, five of them always on watch in the tent set up over the sword and stone.

At Candlemas, many more great lords gathered in London to try to win the sword, but none was able to do so. But Arthur pulled it from the stone as easily at Candlemas as he had at Christmas. And the lords were again aggrieved, and again put the matter in delay until the high feast of Easter.

At Easter, as before, Arthur won the sword. But some of the lords were still unwilling to see Arthur King, and demanded

---

Seneschal: an important and powerful figure in a royal household

Twelfth Day: the twelfth day after Christmas is January 6, the Feast of the Epiphany, which commemorates the arrival of the magi in Bethlehem to see the Christ child

Candlemas: a Christian feast day held on February 2 to honor the presentation of the baby Jesus in the Temple and the purification of the Virgin Mary

a delay until the feast of Pentecost. Then the Archbishop of Canterbury had Merlin gather the best knights who could be found, and whom Uther Pendragon had most loved and trusted, and set them as a bodyguard around Arthur.

At the feast of Pentecost all manner of men tried to pull the sword from the stone. But none succeeded save Arthur, who pulled the sword out in the sight of all the lords and commons. At this, the commons cried together, "We will have Arthur for our King! We will have no more delay, for we see that it is God's will that he should be our King. And we will slay any who still hold against it."

And all kneeled at once, both rich and poor, and begged Arthur's forgiveness for delaying the matter so long. Arthur forgave them. Then he took the sword in both his hands and placed it on the altar where the Archbishop was, and was made knight by the best man there.

Then was the coronation held. Arthur swore to the lords and commons that he would be a true King, and would stand on the side of justice all the days of his life. At the same time he ordered all the lords who held their office from the king to come and pledge their loyalty and service as they ought to do. And many complaints were made to him of great wrongs done since the death of King Uther—of lands taken from the lords, knights, ladies, and gentlemen. Whereupon Arthur ordered the lands to be given again to those that owned them. And when all this was done, he named Sir Kay Seneschal of England.

Within a few years Arthur had won all the north, and Scotland, and all the territory under their control. A part of Wales stood against him, but he overcame all resistance through the noble power of himself and the Knights of the Round Table.

Pentecost: an important Christian feast celebrated the seventh Sunday after Easter to commemorate the Holy Spirit descending upon Jesus's apostles and giving them the ability to speak in tongues

coronation: crowning ceremony

THE DEATH OF ARTHUR

After many brave deeds and glorious achievements, Arthur and his knights came on evil days, for death, misunderstanding, infidelity, and jealousy had demoralized the court of Camelot, leaving it only a shadow of its former self.

The final act of the drama began while Arthur was away in France, fighting an ill-advised campaign against Sir Lancelot, who had once been his closest friend. Sir Mordred, the king's own son, had long envied and hated his father. Traitorously pretending that Arthur had been killed in France, he had himself crowned king in London. When word came from France that Arthur still lived, and was returning to England, Mordred gathered an army. The people, says Malory, "were better pleased with Sir Mordred than they were with king Arthur, and much people drew unto Sir Mordred, and said they would abide with him for better and for worse."

Mordred tried to keep the king from landing at Dover, but Arthur's returning army swept the traitor from the beaches, at great cost to both sides. While Mordred gathered more fighting men from the area around London, Arthur appealed to Lancelot for help in the name of their former friendship, and the two armies prepared for the last great battle.

On Trinity Sunday night, Arthur, lying between sleep and waking, dreamed this dream: That Gawain came to him and said, "Sir, God has given me leave to warn you of your death. Know you

---

infidelity: unfaithfulness

demoralized: discouraged; depressed

Camelot: in Arthurian legend, the capital of King Arthur's kingdom, known as a place of great justice and righteousness

Sir Lancelot: one of the bravest and most noble knights of the Round Table, who falls in love with Arthur's queen, Guinevere

Sir Mordred: the son and eventual enemy of Arthur

abide: continue; stay

Dover: a port town on the southern coast of England; Dover is just across the English Channel from France

Trinity Sunday: the eighth Sunday after Easter, when Christians celebrate the doctrine of the Holy Trinity

Gawain: a nephew of King Arthur and one of the greatest knights of the Round Table

this: if you fight with Sir Mordred tomorrow morning, as you both plan, you will be slain, and so will the greatest part of the people on both sides. God has sent me of his special grace to warn you not to do battle tomorrow, but to make a treaty instead, for a month and a day. Make large offers to bring a truce, for within a month Sir Lancelot will come with all his noble knights and rescue you, and will slay Sir Mordred and all who hold with him."

Then Gawain vanished, and the King called his lords and told them the dream. He then commanded Sir Lucan and his brother Sir Bedivere, with two bishops, to make a treaty with Sir Mordred for a month and a day, at any cost.

After long bargaining, Sir Mordred agreed to accept Cornwall and Kent during Arthur's life, and all England after. It was then agreed that King Arthur and Sir Mordred should meet between the armies, each bringing with him fourteen persons.

When this word was brought to Arthur, he was glad, and went into the field to meet Sir Mordred. But he warned his army that, should they see any sword drawn, they should charge fiercely and slay Sir Mordred, for he did not trust the traitor. Mordred gave the same charge to his army: should they see a sword drawn, they were to charge fiercely, for he knew his father wanted vengeance on him, and he in no way trusted the treaty. And so Arthur and Mordred met as the appointment had been made. They were in complete accord, and wine was brought and they drank.

But then there came a little adder out of a heath bush, and it stung one of the knights in the foot. When the knight felt the sting, he drew his sword to slay the serpent, thinking of no other harm. But when the armies saw the sword drawn, they sounded their trumpets and shouted furiously, and so the battle began.

"Alas, this unlucky day!" said Arthur, and rode back to his party, while Mordred joined his own army.

Sir Lucan: a knight of the Round Table
Sir Bevidere: a knight of the Round Table
Cornwall and Kent: two regions of southern Britain
accord: agreement
adder: a poisonous snake

Never had there been a sadder battle in Christian land. There was rushing and riding, thrusting and striking, with many a grim word and many a deadly stroke. King Arthur rode through the battle many times, in great danger that day.

The battle raged till nightfall, until the knights were laid to the cold earth and a hundred thousand dead lay on the ground. Then was Arthur wrathful beyond measure when he saw his people so slain. He looked around him and saw that of all his army and all his good knights, only two were left alive—Sir Lucan and Sir Bedivere, and they were sore wounded.

Then Arthur saw where Sir Mordred leaned on his sword among a great heap of dead men.

"Give me my spear," said Arthur to Sir Lucan, "For yonder is the traitor that has worked all this woe!"

"Sir, let him be," said Sir Lucan. "He is a bringer of ill luck. If you but live through this cursed day, you will have been revenged on him. Remember what the spirit of Gawain told you this night. God has of his great goodness preserved you so far. If you leave off now, this wicked day of destiny is past."

But the King took the spear in both hands and ran toward Mordred crying, "Traitor, now is thy death day come!"

When Mordred heard King Arthur, he rushed toward him with drawn sword in hand. King Arthur struck him under his shield with a thrust that carried the spear clear through Mordred's body. When Mordred felt his death wound, he thrust himself along the spear, right up to the haft, and holding his sword in both his hands, he struck his father on the side of the head, so that the sword pierced helmet and skull. Then Mordred fell to the earth stark dead, and the noble Arthur fell in a swoon.

Sir Lucan and Sir Bedivere lifted him up, and weakly led him between them to a little chapel not far from the seaside. There the King felt more at ease. But Sir Lucan and Sir Bedivere heard looters in the field killing the wounded and robbing the slain, so they thought it better to bring the King to some town. Since Arthur

---

wrathful: angry
haft: handle
swoon: a fainting spell

could not stand, Sir Lucan lifted him on one side and Sir Bedivere on the other. But the King swooned, and Lucan, by reason of his wounds, himself fell and died. And Bedivere mourned his brother.

Coming to himself again, the King said, "My end comes fast. Take my good sword Excalibur to the water side, and throw it in the water. Then come and tell me what you see."

So Bedivere went to do the King's will. But on the way he looked at the noble sword, its pommel and haft all of precious stones, and said to himself, "If I throw this rich sword in the water, no good will come of it, but much loss." So he hid Excalibur under a tree, and returned to the King and told him that he had thrown the sword in the water.

"What saw you there?" asked the King.

"Sir," he said, "I saw nothing but waves and winds."

"You have not spoken the truth," said the King. "Go again, quickly! As you are near and dear to me, spare not, but throw it in!"

So Bedivere turned back again, and took the sword in his hand. But he thought it a sin and a shame to throw away that noble sword, so he hid it again and again returned to the King and told him that he had been at the water and had done as he commanded.

"What saw you there?" asked the King.

"Sir," he said, "I saw nothing but the ebbing waters and the lapping waves."

"Traitor untrue!" said Arthur. "Who would have thought that you would betray me twice for the richness of the sword? Now go again—and swiftly! Your long delay has put me in jeopardy of my life, for I have taken cold. If you do not now do as I bid you, I will slay you with my own hands!"

So Bedivere departed, and quickly took the sword and went to the water side. There he bound the belt round the hilt, and threw the sword as far into the water as he might.

Excalibur: the legendary sword of King Arthur, which, in Arthurian legend, Arthur
    received in an hour of need from the Lady of the Lake
pommel: handgrip

And there came a hand above the water, and met the sword and caught it, shook it thrice, then vanished with it into the water. Then Bedivere returned to the King and told him what he saw.

"Alas," said the King, "help me hence, for I am afraid I have tarried overlong."

Then Sir Bedivere took the King upon his back, and went with him to the water side. And there came a boat to the shore with many fair ladies in it, and among them all was a Queen, who was the Lady of the Lake, who had done much for Arthur.

And three other Queens were with her: one was Arthur's sister, Morgan le Fay; one was the Queen of Northgalis; and the third was the Queen of the Wastelands. All wore black hoods, and wept when they saw King Arthur.

"Now put me in the boat," said the King.

Sir Bedivere did so, gently. The King laid his head in the lap of Queen Morgan le Fay, who said, "Brother, why have you waited so long? Alas, this wound on your head has caught overmuch cold!"

And so they rowed away from the land, while Bedivere watched. Then he called, "My lord Arthur, what shall become of me now that you go from me and leave me among my enemies?"

"Comfort yourself," said the King, "and do as well as you can. There is in me no strength left to trust in. I go to the vale of Avalon to heal me of my grievous wound. If you hear no more of me, pray for my soul."

And the ladies wept, for it was sad to hear.

When Bedivere had lost sight of the boat, he too wept, and took to the forest. He went on all that night, and in the morning found a chapel and a hermitage between two woods. He went to the chapel, where he found a hermit kneeling by a new-carved tomb. When the hermit saw Bedivere, he knew him, for he was himself the former Archbishop of Canterbury whom Mordred had forced to flee.

---

tarried: waited; delayed
Morgan le Fay: a powerful sorceress and half sister of King Arthur
Queen of Northgalis: the queen of a kingdom in northern Wales
Queen of the Wastelands: the queen of a legendary area where Arthurian knights
    searched for the Holy Grail
vale of Avalon: in Celtic mythology, a valley on an island paradise
hermitage: a secluded dwelling, often inhabited by religious people
hermit: a person who has chosen to live in seclusion, away from other people

"Sir," said Bedivere, "What man is buried here, for whom you pray?"

"Fair son," answered the hermit, "I cannot say. This night at midnight came a number of ladies, and brought hither a corpse, and prayed me to bury him. Here they offered a hundred tapers, and gave me a hundred bezants."

"Alas," said Bedivere, "it is my lord Arthur who lies buried here in this chapel." And he prayed the hermit that he might stay there with him in fasting and prayer, praying for his lord Arthur.

Then Bedivere told the hermit all you have heard before; and he himself put on poor clothes, and served the hermit humbly in fasting and prayer.

Of Arthur's death the authorized texts say only that he was taken away by ladies in a ship, as we have told above. Beyond this, we have the story that Sir Bedivere told: that the ladies bore Arthur to his burial at the chapel. The hermit who had been Archbishop of Canterbury bore witness that someone was buried in the chapel; but he did not know for certain that the body was truly Arthur's.

Some men still say in parts of England that Arthur is not dead, but is kept by the will of the Lord Jesus in another place. Many say that he will come again, and that there is written on his tomb this verse, in Latin:

HERE LIES ARTHUR, THE ONCE AND FUTURE KING.

---

hither: here
tapers: tall, thin candles
bezants: gold coins

PULLING UP THE BAOBAB TREE,
from SUNDIATA: AN EPIC OF OLD MALI

told by D.T. Niane, translated by G.D. Pickett

*The Mali Empire was a thriving and wealthy kingdom in West Africa
from about 1200 to 1600. The following legend focuses on the childhood of
one of Mali's greatest heroes, Sundiata, who was also known as Sogolon
Djata, Mari Djata, and Djata. Sundiata was the son of Naré Maghan, the
king of Mali, and Sogolon Kedjou, his second wife.*

God has his mysteries, which none can fathom. You, perhaps, will
be a king. You can do nothing about it. You, on the other hand,
will be unlucky, but you can do nothing about that either. Each
man finds his way already marked out for him, and he can change
nothing of it.

Sogolon's son had a slow and difficult childhood. At the age of
three he still crawled along on all fours, while children of the same
age were already walking. He had nothing of the great beauty of
his father, Naré Maghan. He had a head so big that he seemed
unable to support it; he also had large eyes, which would open
wide whenever anyone entered his mother's house. He was taciturn
and used to spend the whole day just sitting in the middle of the
house. Whenever his mother went out, he would crawl on all fours
to rummage about the calabashes in search of food, for he was very
greedy.

Malicious tongues began to blab. What three-year-old has not yet
taken his first steps? What three-year-old is not the despair of his
parents through his whims and shifts of mood? What three-year-

---

fathom: understand; comprehend
taciturn: quiet; reserved
rummage: search; look through
calabashes: vines whose fruits are gourds that can be harvested and used as food or
    as containers
malicious: mean; cruel

old is not the joy of his circle through his backwardness in talking? Sogolon Djata (for it was thus that they called him, prefixing his mother's name to his), Sogolon Djata, then, was very different from others of his own age. He spoke little and his severe face never relaxed into a smile. You would have thought that he was already thinking, and what amused children of his age bored him. Often Sogolon would make some of them come to him to keep him company. These children were already walking, and she hoped that Djata, seeing his companions walking, would be tempted to do likewise. But nothing came of it. Besides, Sogolon Djata would brain the poor little things with his already strong arms, and none of them would come near him anymore.

The king's first wife was the first to rejoice at Sogolon Djata's infirmity. Her own son, Dankaran Touman, was already eleven. He was a fine and lively boy, who spent the day running about the village with those of his own age. He had even begun his initiation in the bush. The king had had a bow made for him, and he used to go behind the town to practice archery with his companions. Sassouma was quite happy and snapped her fingers at Sogolon, whose child was still crawling on the ground. Whenever the latter happened to pass by her house, she would say, "Come, my son, walk, jump, leap about. The jinni didn't promise you anything out of the ordinary, but I prefer a son who walks on his two legs to a lion that crawls on the ground." She spoke thus whenever Sogolon went by her door. The innuendo would go straight home, and then she would burst into laughter, that diabolical laughter which a jealous woman knows how to use so well.

Her son's infirmity weighed heavily upon Sogolon Kedjou; she had resorted to all her talent as a sorceress to give strength to her

brain: hit on the head
infirmity: frailty; weakness
initiation in the bush: In some African cultures, boys around the ages of 11 or 12 go into the wild (bush) with their elders to learn the customs of their culture to prepare to become men.
Sassouma: the king's first wife
jinni: supernatural spirits believed to be able to predict and influence what will happen in a person's life
innuendo: an insinuation; a veiled or indirect insult
diabolical: evil

son's legs, but the rarest herbs had been useless. The king himself lost hope.

Sogolon Kedjou and her children lived on the queen mother's leftovers, but she kept a little garden in the open ground behind the village. It was there that she passed her brightest moments looking after her onions and gnougous. One day she happened to be short of condiments and went to the queen mother to beg a little baobab leaf.

"Look you," said the malicious Sassouma, "I have a calabash full. Help yourself, you poor woman. As for me, my son knew how to walk at seven, and it was he who went and picked these baobab leaves. Take them, then, since your son is unequal to mine." Then she laughed derisively with that fierce laughter which cuts through your flesh and penetrates right to the bone.

Sogolon Kedjou was dumbfounded. She had never imagined that hate could be so strong in a human being. With a lump in her throat, she left Sassouma's. Outside her hut Mari Djata, sitting on his useless legs, was blandly eating out of a calabash. Unable to contain herself any longer, Sogolon burst into sobs and, seizing a piece of wood, hit her son.

"Oh son of misfortune, will you never walk? Through your fault I have just suffered the greatest affront of my life! What have I done, God, for you to punish me in this way?"

Mari Djata seized the piece of wood and, looking at his mother, said, "Mother, what's the matter?"

"Shut up, nothing can ever wash me clean of this insult."

"But what, then?"

"Sassouma has just humiliated me over a matter of a baobab leaf. At your age her own son could walk and used to bring his mother baobab leaves."

"Cheer up, Mother, cheer up."

"No. It's too much. I can't."

---

gnougous: a plant that can be eaten
condiments: seasonings for food
baobab: a common African tree that has edible leaves and fruit
derisively: scornfully
dumbfounded: surprised to the point of being speechless
affront: insult

"Very well, then, I am going to walk today," said Mari Djata. "Go and tell my father's smiths to make me the heaviest possible iron rod. Mother, do you want just the leaves of the baobab, or would you rather I brought you the whole tree?"

"Ah, my son, to wipe out this insult, I want the tree and its roots at my feet outside my hut."

Balla Fasséké, who was present, ran to the master smith, Farakourou, to order an iron rod.

Sogolon had sat down in front of her hut. She was weeping softly and holding her head between her two hands. Mari Djata went calmly back to his calabash of rice and began eating again as if nothing had happened. From time to time he looked up discreetly at his mother, who was murmuring in a low voice, "I want the whole tree in front of my hut, the whole tree."

All of a sudden a voice burst into laughter behind the hut. It was the wicked Sassouma telling one of her serving women about the scene of humiliation, and she was laughing loudly so that Sogolon could hear. Sogolon fled into the hut and hid her face under the blankets so as not to have before her eyes this heedless boy, who was more preoccupied with eating than with anything else. With her head buried in the bedclothes, Sogolon wept, and her body shook violently. Her daughter, Sogolon Djamarou, had come and sat down beside her, and she said, "Mother, Mother, don't cry. Why are you crying?"

Mari Djata had finished eating, and dragging himself along on his legs, he came and sat under the wall of the hut, for the sun was scorching. What was he thinking about? He alone knew.

The royal forges were situated outside the walls, and over a hundred smiths worked there. The bows, spears, arrows, and shields of Niani's warriors came from there. When Balla Fasséké came to order the iron rod, Farakourou said to him, "The great day has arrived, then?"

---

smiths: metalworkers
discreetly: subtly; quietly
heedless: oblivious; unaware
forges: workshops of metalworkers
Niani: the small kingdom in Mali where this story takes place

"Yes. Today is a day like any other, but it will see what no other day has seen."

The master of the forges, Farakourou, was the son of the old Nounfaïri, and he was a soothsayer like his father. In his workshops there was an enormous iron bar wrought by his father, Nounfaïri. Everybody wondered what this bar was destined to be used for. Farakourou called six of his apprentices and told them to carry the iron bar to Sogolon's house.

When the smiths put the gigantic iron bar down in front of the hut, the noise was so frightening that Sogolon, who was lying down, jumped up with a start. Then Balla Fasséké, son of Gnankouman Doua, spoke.

"Here is the great day, Mari Djata. I am speaking to you, Maghan, son of Sogolon. The waters of the Niger can efface the stain from the body, but they cannot wipe out an insult. Arise, young lion, roar, and may the bush know that from henceforth it has a master."

The apprentice smiths were still there, Sogolon had come out, and everyone was watching Mari Djata. He crept on all fours and came to the iron bar. Supporting himself on his knees and one hand, with the other hand he picked up the iron bar without any effort and stood it up vertically. Now he was resting on nothing but his knees and held the bar with both his hands. A deathly silence had gripped all those present. Sogolon Djata closed his eyes, held tight; the muscles in his arms tensed. With a violent jerk he threw his weight onto the bar and his knees left the ground. Sogolon Kedjou was all eyes and watched her son's legs, which were trembling as though from an electric shock. Djata was sweating, and the sweat ran from his brow. In a great effort, he straightened up and was on his feet at one go—but the great bar of iron was twisted and had taken the form of a bow!

---

soothsayer: fortune-teller
wrought: shaped
the Niger: the Niger River, one of the largest rivers in Western Africa
efface: take away
henceforth: this day forward

Then Balla Fasséké sang out the "Hymn to the Bow," striking up with his powerful voice:

Take your bow, Simbon,
Take your bow and let us go.
Take your bow, Sogolon Djata.

When Sogolon saw her son standing, she stood dumb for a moment; then suddenly she sang these words of thanks to God, who had given her son the use of his legs:

Oh day, what a beautiful day,
Oh day, day of joy;
Allah Almighty, you never created a finer day.
So my son is going to walk!

Standing in the position of a soldier at ease, Sogolon Djata, supported by his enormous rod, was sweating great beads of sweat. Balla Fasséké's song had alerted the whole palace; people came running from all over to see what had happened, and each stood bewildered before Sogolon's son. The queen mother had rushed there, and when she saw Mari Djata standing up, she trembled from head to foot. After recovering his breath, Sogolon's son dropped the bar and the crowd stood to one side. His first steps were those of a giant. Balla Fasséké fell into step, and pointing his finger at Djata, he cried:

Room, room, make room!
The lion has walked;
Hide, antelopes,
Get out of his way.

Simbon: a term of respect for a great hunter
Allah: Islamic name for God

Behind Niani there was a young baobab tree, and it was there that the children of the town came to pick leaves for their mothers. With all his might the son of Sogolon tore up the tree and put it on his shoulders and went back to his mother. He threw the tree in front of the hut and said, "Mother, here are some baobab leaves for you. From henceforth it will be outside your hut that the women of Niani will come to stock up."

from THE INGENIOUS GENTLEMAN DON QUIXOTE OF LA MANCHA

Miguel de Cervantes Saavedra

Don Quixote *is the masterwork of Miguel de Cervantes Saavedra (1547–1616), a Spanish poet, dramatist, and novelist. The novel—the complete title of which is* El ingenioso hidalgo Don Quijote de la Mancha, *or* The Ingenious Gentleman Don Quixote of La Mancha—*relates the misadventures of an aging, idealistic, retired Spanish landowner who is so deeply absorbed in medieval romance stories that he imagines himself to be a knight.*

In its original form, the novel fills more than a thousand closely printed pages. It was published in two parts, the first in 1605 and the second in 1615. Considered by many to be the first modern novel, Don Quixote *contains elements of narrative fiction that would influence later generations of authors, and would inspire artists and composers to depict the hero in paintings and music. The novel was wildly popular in its time and has since been translated into many languages.*

The following chapters are from an 1885 English translation by John Ormsby, abridged by Mabel F. Wheaton, and slightly adapted by the editors of this volume. This excerpt from the beginning of the novel introduces Don Quixote and describes one of his most famous adventures.

CHAPTER 1
WHICH TREATS OF THE CHARACTER AND PURSUITS OF THE FAMOUS GENTLEMAN DON QUIXOTE OF LA MANCHA

In a village of La Mancha, the name of which I have no desire to call to mind, there lived not long since one of those gentlemen that keep a lance in the lance-rack, an old buckler, a lean hack, and

---

La Mancha: a district in the south-central part of Spain
buckler: a kind of shield
hack: a horse let out for hire or used in various kinds of work

a greyhound for hunting. A stew of rather more beef than mutton, a salad on most nights, scraps on Saturdays, lentils on Fridays, and a pigeon or so extra on Sundays, made away with three quarters of his income. The rest of it went in a doublet of fine cloth and velvet breeches and shoes to match for holidays, while on weekdays he made a brave figure in his best homespun. He had in his house a housekeeper past forty, a niece under twenty, and a lad for the field and market-place.

The age of this gentleman of ours was bordering on fifty. He was of a hardy habit, spare, gaunt, a very early riser, and fond of hunting. Some said his name was Quijada or Quesada, though there is some difference of opinion on that matter. But it seems likely that he was called Quejana. This, however, is of but little importance to our tale, so long as in the telling of it we stray not a hair's breadth from the truth.

Whenever this gentleman was at leisure, which was mostly all the year round, he gave himself up to reading books of chivalry with such enthusiasm that he almost entirely neglected the pursuit of hunting and the management of his property. To such a pitch did his infatuation go that he sold many an acre of good land to buy books of chivalry to read, and brought home as many of them as he could get.

Of all these books there were none he liked so well as those of the famous Feliciano de Silva. Their clarity of style and ingenious turns of phrase were as pearls in his sight, particularly when in his reading he came upon passages like "the reason of the unreason with which my reason is afflicted so weakens my reason that with reason I murmur at your beauty"; or, "the high heavens, that of your divinity divinely fortify you with the stars, render you deserving of the desert your greatness deserves." Over pleasantries

---

lentils: a kind of small pea
doublet: a close-fitting garment for men, worn in Western Europe from the 15th to
     the 17th century, covering the body from the neck to the waist, or a little below
homespun: plain, coarse cloth
gaunt: very thin
chivalry: in Europe in the Middle Ages, a code of conduct that spelled out the
     virtues that knights should follow, including loyalty, bravery, and protecting
     the weak and powerless
infatuation: foolish and excessive devotion

of this sort the poor gentleman lost his wits, and used to lie awake striving to understand them.

Many a long discussion did he have with the curate of his village, a learned man, as to which had been the better knight, Palmerin of England or Amadis of Gaul. But Master Nicholas, the village barber, used to say that neither of them came up to the Knight of Phoebus. In short, our gentleman became so absorbed in his books that he spent his nights from sunset to sunrise, and his days from dawn to dark, poring over them. With so little sleep and so much reading, his brains got so dry that he lost his mind. His fancy grew full of what he read about in his books—enchantments, quarrels, battles, challenges, wounds, wooings, loves, agonies, and all sorts of impossible nonsense; and it so possessed his mind that the whole fabric of invention and fancy he read of seemed true. To him, no history in the world had more reality in it.

His wits being quite gone, he hit upon the strangest notion that any madman in this world has ever had. He fancied it was right and necessary, for both the support of his own honor and the service of his country, that he should make a knight-errant of himself, roaming the world in full armor and on horseback in quest of adventures, and putting in practice all that he had read of as being the usual practices of knights-errant—righting every kind of wrong, and exposing himself to peril and danger from which he would gain eternal renown and fame. And so, led away by the intense enjoyment he found in these pleasant fancies, he put his scheme into execution.

The first thing he did was to clean up some armor that had belonged to his great-grandfather, and had been for ages lying forgotten in a corner eaten with rust and covered with mildew. He scoured and polished it as best he could. But he perceived one great defect in it, that the helmet was more like a hat and would not close to cover his face. This problem, however, his ingenuity solved, for he contrived to cut some pieces of cardboard to supply the missing parts. In order to see if it was strong and fit to stand a cut, he drew

---

curate: clergyman; parson
knight-errant: a wandering knight going about in search of adventure

his sword and gave it a couple of slashes, the first of which undid in an instant what had taken him a week to do.

The ease with which he had knocked it to pieces discouraged him somewhat, and to guard against that danger he set to work fixing bars of iron on the inside until he was satisfied with its strength. And then, not caring to try any more experiments with it, he adopted it as a helmet of the most perfect construction.

He next proceeded to inspect his hack, which, though all skin and bones, surpassed in his eyes Bucephalus of Alexander. He spent four days in thinking what name to give the animal, because (as he said to himself) it was not right that a horse belonging to a knight so famous, and one with such merits of his own, should be without some distinctive name. For it was only reasonable that, his master taking a new character, the horse should have a new name, and that it should be a distinguished and full-sounding one, befitting the new calling he was about to follow. And so, after having composed, struck out, rejected, added to, unmade, and remade a multitude of names out of his memory and fancy, he decided upon calling his horse Rocinante. To his thinking, this name was lofty, sonorous, and significant of the creature's condition as a hack before he became what he now was, the first and foremost of all the hacks in the world.

Having got a name for his horse so much to his taste, he was anxious to get one for himself. He spent eight days more pondering over this point, till at last he made up his mind to call himself Don Quixote of La Mancha, which, he believed, both accurately described his country of origin and did honor to it in taking his name from it.

So then, his armor being furnished, his hack christened, and he himself properly named, he came to the conclusion that nothing more was needed now but to look out for a lady to be in love with, for a knight-errant without love was like a tree without leaves or fruit, or a body without a soul.

Bucephalus: war horse of the fourth-century conqueror Alexander the Great
Rocinante: *rocin* is the Spanish word for a horse employed in labor, as distinguished from one kept for pleasure, and may be translated "hack"; *ante* is a Latin form of the Spanish *antes*, meaning "before"; thus *Rocinante* means "formerly, or before, a hack"

"If," he said to himself, "for punishment of my sins, or by my good fortune, I should come across some giant hereabouts—a common occurrence with knights-errant—and overthrow him in one onslaught, or cut him in two, or, in short, vanquish and subdue him, would it not be well to have some one I may send him to as a present, that he may come in and fall on his knees before my sweet lady, and in a humble, submissive voice say, 'I am the giant Caraculiambro, lord of the island of Malindrania, vanquished in single combat by the knight beyond all praise, Don Quixote of La Mancha, who has commanded me to present myself before your grace, that your highness may dispose of me at your pleasure'?"

Oh, how our good gentleman enjoyed the delivery of this speech, especially when he had thought of some one to call his lady! There was, in a village near his own, a very good-looking farm girl with whom he had been at one time in love, though she never knew it nor gave a thought to the matter. Her name was Aldonza Lorenzo. Upon her he thought fit to confer the title of Lady of his Thoughts. After some search for a name which should not be out of harmony with her own, and should suggest and indi-cate that of a princess and great lady, he decided upon calling her Dulcinea del Toboso—she being of El Toboso—a name, to his mind, musical, uncommon, and significant, like all those he had already bestowed upon himself and the things belonging to him.

Chapter 2
Which Treats of the First Sally the Ingenious Don Quixote Made from Home

Having made these preparations, he did not wish to delay putting his plan into action, urged on by the thought of all the world was losing by his delay, as there were so many wrongs to right, injustices to repair, abuses to remove, and duties to perform. So, without giving notice of his intention to any one, and without anybody seeing him, one morning before the dawn of the day (which was one of the hottest of the month of July), he donned his

---

sally: an excursion; a venturing forth, usually off the beaten path
donned: put on

suit of armor and his patched-up helmet, mounted Rocinante, took his shield and lance, and by the back door of the yard sallied forth upon the plain. It was with the highest contentment and satisfaction that he saw how easily he had made a beginning toward the fulfillment of his grand purpose.

But scarcely did he find himself upon the open plain when a terrible thought struck him, one all but enough to make him abandon the enterprise at the very outset. It occurred to him that he had not been dubbed a knight, and that according to the law of chivalry he neither could nor ought to bear arms against any other knight.

These reflections made him waver in his purpose, but his madness being stronger than any reasoning, he made up his mind to have himself dubbed a knight by the first person he came across, following the example of so many others in the books he had read. And so comforting himself he pursued his way, letting his horse take whatever path it chose, for in this he believed lay the essence of adventures.

Thus our new-fledged adventurer paced along, talking to himself and saying, "Who knows but that in time to come, when the true history of my famous deeds is made known, the sage who writes it, when he has to set forth my first sally in the early morning, will do it after this fashion? 'Scarce had the rubicund Apollo spread o'er the face of the broad spacious earth the golden threads of his bright hair, scarce had the little birds of painted plumage attuned their notes to hail with dulcet and mellifluous harmony the coming of the rosy Dawn, when the renowned knight Don Quixote of La Mancha mounted his celebrated steed Rocinante and began to traverse the ancient and famous Plain of Montiel'" — which in fact he was actually traversing.

----

dubbed a knight: part of a ceremony to confer knighthood, in which the kneeling
    candidate received a tap on the shoulder with the flat side of a sword
sage: wise
rubicund: ruddy; reddish
Apollo: mythological ancient Greek and Roman god of light, music, and poetry
dulcet: sweet to the ear
mellifluous: flowing sweetly or smoothly
traverse: to travel across or over

Presently he broke out again, as if he were love-stricken in earnest, "O Princess Dulcinea, lady of this captive heart, a grievous wrong hast thou done me to drive me forth with scorn, and banish me from the presence of thy beauty. O lady, hold in remembrance this heart, thy vassal, that thus in anguish pines for love of thee."

So he went on stringing together these and other absurdities, all in the style of those his books had taught him, imitating their language as well as he could. And all the while he rode so slowly and the sun mounted so rapidly that it was enough to melt his brains if he had any. Nearly all day he traveled without anything remarkable happening to him, at which he was in despair, for he was anxious to encounter some one upon whom to try the might of his strong arm.

He was on the road all day, and towards nightfall his hack and he found themselves dead tired and hungry. Looking all around to see if he could discover any castle or shepherd's hut where he might refresh himself and relieve his sore wants, he perceived not far off the road an inn, which was as welcome as a star guiding him to redemption. Quickening his pace, he reached it just as night was setting in. At the door were standing two young women, girls "of the district" as they call them, on their way to Seville with some mule drivers who had chanced to halt that night at the inn.

For our adventurer, everything he thought or imagined came from the pages of the storybooks he had read; so, it seemed to him that the inn was a shining castle with four great towers, not forgetting the moat and drawbridge and all the trappings that went with castles of the sort. To this inn, which to him seemed a castle, he advanced. A short distance from it, he brought Rocinante to a halt, and waited for some dwarf to sound a trumpet to give notice that a knight was approaching the castle, for so it always happened in the books he had read. But seeing that they were slow about it, and that Rocinante was in a hurry to reach the stable, he proceeded to

---

presently: very soon

vassal: subject; servant

moat: deep ditch surrounding a castle, filled with water

drawbridge: movable bridge at a castle's main entrance, raised by chains and
    lowered over the moat to allow entrance within the castle walls

the inn door, where he perceived the two damsels standing there, who seemed to him to be two fair maidens or lovely ladies taking their ease at the castle gate.

At this moment a swineherd came along, driving his pigs—for, without any apology, that is what they were. He gave a blast of his horn to bring them together, and it seemed to Don Quixote to be what he was expecting, the signal of some dwarf announcing his arrival. And so with great satisfaction he rode up to the inn. The girls, seeing a man of this sort approaching in full armor and with lance and shield, turned to flee within.

Don Quixote, guessing their fear, raised his cardboard visor, which revealed his dry, dusty face. With courteous bearing and gentle voice, he addressed them: "Your ladyships need not fly or fear any rudeness, for it is no part of the order of knighthood which I profess to wrong anyone, much less such high-born maidens as your appearance proclaims you to be." The girls were straining their eyes to make out the features which the clumsy visor hid, but they could not restrain their laughter, which made Don Quixote take offense and say, "Modesty becomes the fair, and laughter that has little cause is great silliness; this, however, I say not to pain or anger you, for my desire is none other than to serve you."

The incomprehensible language and the unpromising looks of our knight only increased the girls' laughter, which increased his irritation. Matters might have taken a bad turn but at that moment the innkeeper came out, a very fat and peaceful man. Seeing this bizarre figure clad in oddly unmatched bits of armor, he was inclined to join the damsels in their amusement. But, suspicious of the warlike appearance of his visitor, he thought it best to speak civilly. So he said, "Sir Knight, if your worship wants lodging, except for a bed—for there is not one in the inn—there is plenty of everything else here."

Don Quixote, observing the respectful bearing of the governor of the castle (for so the innkeeper seemed in his eyes), replied, "Sir Keeper of the Castle, for me anything will suffice.

visor: lower part of a helmet, which lifts or opens to show the face

28

My armor is my only wear,
My only rest the fray."

"In that case," said the host,

"Your bed is on the flinty rock,
Your sleep to watch away."

So saying, he advanced to hold the stirrup for Don Quixote, who got down with great difficulty and exertion, for he had not eaten all day. Our knight then charged the host to take great care of his horse, as he was the best steed in this world. The innkeeper eyed Rocinante, but did not find him even half as good as Don Quixote said.

After putting the animal in the stable, the innkeeper returned to see what might be wanted by his guest. The damsels had by this time made their peace with him, and were now helping to remove his armor. They had taken off his breastplate and backpiece, but they neither knew nor saw how to remove his makeshift helmet, for he had fastened it with green ribbons, which, as there was no untying the knots, had to be cut. This, however, he would not by any means allow, so he remained all the evening with his helmet on, the oddest and most laughable figure that can be imagined.

Don Quixote fancied that the girls who were helping to remove his armor must be ladies of high degree of the castle, so he said to them with much delicacy and wit,

"Oh, never, surely, was there knight
So served by any dame,
As served was Don Quixote
When from his town he came;
With maidens to wait on his every need,
And princesses caring for his steed...."

The girls, who were not used to hearing speeches of this sort, had nothing to say in reply, so they only asked him if he wanted anything to eat. "I would gladly eat a bit of something," said Don

---

fray: armed contest; combat; battle

Quixote, "for I feel it would be most welcome." The day happened to be a Friday, and in the whole inn there was nothing but some pieces of fish they call "troutlet," or small trout. So they asked him if he thought he could eat some small troutlet, for there was no other fish to give him.

"If there be troutlets enough," said Don Quixote, "they will be the same thing as a trout. But whatever it be let it come quickly, for the burden and pressure of arms cannot be borne without support to the inside."

They set a table for him at the door of the inn, and the host brought him a portion of ill-soaked and worse-cooked fish, and a piece of bread as black and moldy as his own armor. A laughable sight it was to see him eating, for having his helmet on and the visor up, he could not with his own hands put anything into his mouth unless some one else placed it there. One of the girls provided this service. But to give him anything to drink was impossible, or would have been so had not the innkeeper put one end of a reed in the knight's mouth and poured the wine into the other—all of which Don Quixote bore with patience rather than cut the ribbons of his helmet.

While this was going on, a swineherd passed the inn and sounded his horn four or five times, and thereby completely convinced Don Quixote that he was in some famous castle, and that they were entertaining him with music, and that the fish was the finest trout, the bread white and fresh, the peasant girls fine ladies, and the innkeeper the governor of the castle. But still it distressed him to think he had not been dubbed a knight, for it was plain to him he could not lawfully engage in any adventure without receiving the order of knighthood.

CHAPTER 3
WHEREIN IS RELATED THE AMUSING WAY IN WHICH DON QUIXOTE HAD HIMSELF DUBBED A KNIGHT

Troubled by this reflection, he hastily finished his scanty supper and called the innkeeper to him. Shutting himself into the stable with him, Don Quixote fell on his knees and said, "From this spot I rise not, noble sir, until your courtesy grants me the boon I seek, one that will proclaim your praise and benefit the human race."

The innkeeper, seeing his guest at his feet and hearing a speech of this kind, stood staring at him in bewilderment, not knowing what to do or say, and urging him to rise, but all to no purpose. At last he agreed to grant the boon demanded of him.

"I expected no less, my lord, from your High Magnificence," replied Don Quixote. "The boon I have asked, and which your generosity has granted, is that tonight I be allowed to keep watch over my arms in the chapel of this your castle; and tomorrow morning that you shall dub me a knight, thus enabling me lawfully to roam through all the four quarters of the world seeking adventures on behalf of those in distress, as is the duty of chivalry and of knights-errant like myself, whose ambition is directed to such deeds."

The innkeeper, who, as has been mentioned, had some suspicion of the state of his guest's wits, decided to humor him. So he told Don Quixote that he was quite right in pursuing such a goal, and that he himself in his younger days had followed the same honorable calling, roaming in quest of adventures in various parts of the world, until at last he had retired to this castle of his, where he received all knights-errant, of whatever rank or condition they might be. Moreover, the innkeeper told him that in this castle there was no chapel in which he could keep watch over his armor, as it had been pulled down in order to be rebuilt, but that he might keep watch in a courtyard of the castle. And in the morning, God willing, the ceremonies might be performed to have him dubbed a knight, and so thoroughly dubbed that nobody could be more so.

The innkeeper then asked if he had any money with him, to which Don Quixote replied that he had not a cent, as in all the stories of knights-errant he had never read of any of them carrying any money. On this point the innkeeper told him he was mistaken. Such matters were not mentioned in the stories, said the innkeeper, because the authors saw no need to mention anything so obvious and necessary as money and clean shirts. However, it was not to be therefore supposed that the knights did not carry them.

---

boon: something granted as a benefit or favor

The innkeeper assured Don Quixote that he might regard it as certain that all knights-errant carried well-furnished purses in case of emergency, and likewise carried shirts and a little box of ointment to cure the wounds they received. For in those plains and deserts where they engaged in combat and came out wounded, there was not always someone ready at hand to cure them, unless indeed they had for a friend some magician to aid them at once by fetching through the air upon a cloud some damsel or dwarf with a vial of water of such power that by tasting one drop of it they were cured of their wounds in an instant. The innkeeper therefore advised his guest never to travel without money and the usual necessary articles, as he would find them handy when he least expected it.

Don Quixote promised to follow this advice carefully. It was then promptly arranged that he should watch his armor in a large yard at one side of the inn. So, collecting it all together, Don Quixote placed it on the trough that stood by the side of a well. Bracing his shield on his arm, he grasped his lance and, as night began to fall, proceeded with a stately air to march up and down in front of the trough.

The innkeeper told his other guests of Don Quixote's expectation of being dubbed a knight. Full of wonder at so strange a form of madness, they flocked to see, and observed with what composure he sometimes paced up and down, or sometimes, leaning on his lance, gazed on his armor without taking his eyes off it for ever so long.

Meanwhile one of the mule drivers at the inn needed to water his team. To do so, it was necessary to remove Don Quixote's armor as it lay on the trough. As the man approached, Don Quixote cried out, "O thou, whoever thou art, rash knight that comest to lay hands on the armor of the most valorous man of arms that ever held a sword, have a care what thou dost; touch it not unless thou wouldst lay down thy life as the penalty of thy rashness."

The mule driver ignored these words, though he would have done better to listen if he had cared for his health. Seizing the armor by the straps, he flung it some distance from him. Seeing this, Don

---

vial: small bottle

Quixote raised his eyes to heaven, and fixing his thoughts, apparently, upon his Dulcinea, exclaimed, "Aid me, lady mine, in this my first encounter; let not thy favor and protection fail me in this first peril." With these and similar words, dropping his shield he lifted his lance with both hands and delivered a blow on the mule-driver's head that stretched him on the ground so stunned that, had it been followed by a second blow, there would have been no need of a surgeon to cure the man. This done, Don Quixote picked up his armor and returned to his watch with the same serenity as before.

Shortly after this, another mule-driver, not knowing what had happened (for the first still lay senseless), came with the same object of giving water to his mules, and proceeded to remove the armor in order to clear the trough. Don Quixote, without uttering a word, once more dropped his shield and once more landed a shattering blow with his lance.

At the noise all the people of the inn ran to the spot, and among them the innkeeper. Seeing this, Don Quixote braced his shield on his arm and exclaimed, "O Lady of Beauty, strength and support of my faint heart, it is time for thee to turn the eyes of thy greatness on this thy captive knight on the brink of so mighty an adventure." By this time he felt he would not have flinched if all the mule-drivers in the world had attacked him.

The comrades of the wounded men began to shower stones on Don Quixote, who screened himself as best he could with his shield, not daring to quit the trough and leave his armor unprotected. The innkeeper shouted to them to leave him alone, for he had already told them that the man was mad. Still louder shouted Don Quixote, calling them knaves and traitors.

"You base and vile rabble," he cried, "fling, strike, come on, do all ye can against me, ye shall see what the reward of your folly and insolence will be." This he uttered with so much spirit and boldness that he filled his attackers with such fear that they ceased stoning him. He allowed them to carry off the wounded, and with the same calmness as before resumed the watch over his armor.

But these mad actions were not much to the liking of the innkeeper, who determined to cut matters short and confer upon

---

insolence: rudeness

him at once the unlucky order of knighthood before any further misadventure could occur. So, going up to him, he apologized for the rudeness which had been offered by these low people. As he had already told him, although there was no chapel in the castle, none was needed for what remained to be done, for, as he understood the ceremony, the whole point of being dubbed a knight lay in the slap on the shoulder, and that could be administered in the middle of a field. Moreover, the innkeeper assured Don Quixote that he had now done all that was needed in watching the armor, for all requirements were satisfied by a watch of two hours only, while he had been watching for more than four.

Don Quixote believed all, and told him he stood there ready to obey him, and to make an end of it with as much haste as possible; for, if he were again attacked, and felt himself to be a dubbed knight, he believed he would not leave a soul alive in the castle, except those his host might bid be spared.

The innkeeper promptly brought out a book he used to enter his accounts of the straw and barley which the mule-drivers bought from him. With a lad carrying the stub of a candle, and the two damsels already mentioned, he returned to where Don Quixote stood, and ordered him to kneel. Then, reading from his account-book as if he were repeating some devout prayer, he raised his hand and, with the knight's own sword, gave him a sturdy thwack on the neck, and another smart slap on the shoulder, all the while muttering between his teeth as if saying his prayers. He then directed one of the girls to strap the sword on Don Quixote, which she did with great seriousness, as was required to prevent a burst of laughter at each stage of the ceremony. The girl said to him, "May God make your worship a very fortunate knight, and grant you success in battle." Then the other girl helped him put on his spurs.

Having thus, with hot haste and speed, brought to a conclusion these never-till-now-seen ceremonies, Don Quixote could not wait to be on horseback and sally forth in quest of adventures. After saddling Rocinante, at once he mounted, and, thanking his host for his kindness in knighting him, he addressed him in language so extraordinary that it is impossible to report it. The innkeeper, to get him on his way, replied with language no less flowery though with shorter words, and, without calling upon him to pay the bill, let him go with all good speed.

[In his first adventure, Don Quixote is badly beaten. He is taken home to recover from his wounds, where he is cared for by his niece, and by his friends, the curate and the village barber. They resolve to cure his madness by getting rid of his collection of books of chivalry.]

Chapter 7
Of the Second Sally of Our Worthy Knight Don Quixote of La Mancha

That night the housekeeper burned to ashes, in the yard, all the books that were in the whole house. To remedy their friend's disorder, the curate and the barber immediately began to wall up and plaster the room where the books had been, so that when Don Quixote got up he should not find them. The cause being removed, they hoped the effect might cease, and they might say that a magician had carried them off, room and all; and this was done with all haste.

Two days later Don Quixote got up, and the first thing he did was to go and look for his books. Not finding the room where he had left it, he wandered from side to side looking for it. He came to the place where the door used to be, and tried it with his hands, and turned and twisted his eyes in every direction without saying a word; but after a good while he asked his housekeeper the whereabouts of the room that held his books.

The housekeeper, who had been well instructed in what she was to answer, said, "What room is it that your worship is looking for? There are neither room nor books in this house now, for a magician came on a cloud one night after the day your worship left, and, dismounting from a serpent that he rode, he entered the room. What he did there I know not, but after a while he made off, flying through the roof, and left the house full of smoke; and when we went to see what he had done, we saw neither book nor room. But I remember very well, that on leaving, the old villain said in a loud voice that he had done mischief because of a grudge he held against the owner of the books and the room; and he said, too, that his name was the Sage Munaton."

"He must have said Frestón," said Don Quixote.

"I don't know whether he called himself Frestón or Friton," said the housekeeper, "I only know that his name ended with 'ton.'"

"So it does," said Don Quixote, "and he is a sage magician, a great enemy of mine, who has a spite against me because he knows by his arts and lore that in time I am to engage in single combat with a knight whom he befriends but whom I am to conquer, and he will be unable to prevent it. And for this reason he attempts to do me all the ill turns that he can. But it will be hard for him to oppose or avoid what is decreed by Heaven."

"Who doubts that?" said the niece. "But, uncle, would it not be better to remain at peace in your own house instead of roaming the world, never reflecting that many go for wool and come back shorn?"

"Oh, niece of mine," replied Don Quixote, "how much astray art thou in thy reasoning. Before they can shear me, I shall have plucked away and stripped off the beards of all who would dare to touch even the tip of a hair of mine."

The niece and housekeeper were unwilling to make any further answer, as they saw that his anger was kindling.

In short, then, he remained at home fifteen days very quietly without showing any signs of a desire to take up with his former delusions, and during this time he held lively discussions with the curate and the barber. He maintained that knights-errant were what the world stood most in need of, and that in him was to be accomplished the revival of knight-errantry. The curate sometimes contradicted him, sometimes agreed with him, for if he had not observed this precaution he would have been unable to bring him to reason.

Don Quixote also worked to persuade a neighbor of his, a farm laborer, an honest man but with very little wit in his skull. After many persuasions and promises, the poor rustic made up his mind to sally forth with the knight and serve him as his squire.

---

lore: learning
shorn: having the hair or wool clipped off
rustic: a country person
squire: an attendant on a knight

Don Quixote told him he ought to be ready to go with him gladly, because at any moment an adventure might occur that might win an island in the twinkling of an eye and leave him governor of it. On these and similar promises, Sancho Panza (for so the laborer was called) left wife and children, and engaged himself as squire to his neighbor.

Don Quixote next set about getting some money. Selling one thing and pawning another, and making a bad bargain in every case, he got together a fair sum. After restoring his battered helmet as best he could, he advised his squire Sancho of the day and hour he meant to set out, so that he might supply himself with neces-sary items. Above all, he urged him to take saddle-bags with him. Sancho said he would, and that he meant to take also a very good ass he had, as he was not much given to going on foot.

About the ass, Don Quixote hesitated a little. He tried to call to mind any knight-errant taking with him a squire mounted on an ass, but no instance occurred to his memory. Nevertheless, he determined to take Sancho, with the intention of furnishing him with a more honorable mount when the chance presented itself, by taking the horse of the first discourteous knight he encountered.

Don Quixote provided himself with shirts and such other things as he could, as the innkeeper had advised him. All this being settled and done, one night Don Quixote and Sancho Panza, without taking leave of wife and children or of housekeeper and niece, sallied forth from the village, unseen by anybody. They made such good way that by daylight they felt safe from discovery, even if anyone should search for them.

Sancho rode on his ass like a patriarch with his saddle-bags and wine skin, and longing to see himself soon governor of the island his master had promised him. Don Quixote decided upon taking the road over the Plain of Montiel, which he traveled with less discomfort than on the last occasion, for, as it was early morning and the rays of the sun fell on them at a slant, the heat did not distress them.

---

patriarch: ruler of a family; honored old man
wine skin: leather bag used to hold wine, carried by travelers

And now Sancho Panza said to his master, "Your worship will take care, Sir Knight-errant, not to forget about the island you have promised me, for be it ever so big, I'll be equal to governing it."

To which Don Quixote replied, "Thou must know, friend Sancho Panza, that among the knights-errant of old it was a common practice to make their squires governors of the islands or kingdoms they won, and I am determined that there shall be no failure on my part in so liberal a custom. And if thou livest and I live, it may well be that before six days are over, I will have won some kingdom that has others dependent upon it, which will be just the thing to crown thee king of one of them."

"In that case," said Sancho Panza, "if I should become a king by one of those miracles your worship speaks of, then Theresa Panza, my old woman, would come to be queen and my children princes."

"Well, who doubts it?" said Don Quixote.

"I doubt it," replied Sancho Panza, "because for my part I am persuaded that though God should shower down kingdoms upon earth, not one of them would fit the head of Theresa Panza."

"Leave it to God, Sancho," returned Don Quixote, "for he will give her what suits her best; but do not undervalue thyself so much as to be content with anything less than being governor of a province."

"I will not, sir," answered Sancho, "especially as I have for a master a man of such quality as your worship, who will be able to give me all that will be suitable for me and all that I can bear."

Chapter 8
Of the Good Fortune Which the Valiant Don Quixote Had in the Terrible and Undreamt-of Adventure of the Windmills

At this point they came in sight of thirty or forty windmills standing on the plain, and as soon as Don Quixote saw them he said to his squire, "Fortune is arranging matters for us better than we could have shaped our desires for ourselves. Look there, friend Sancho Panza, where thirty or more monstrous giants present themselves, all of whom I mean to engage in battle and slay, and with whose spoils we shall begin to make our fortunes; for this is righteous warfare, and it is God's good service to sweep so evil a breed from off the face of the earth."

"What giants?" said Sancho Panza.

"Those thou seest there," answered his master, "with the long arms, some of them nearly two leagues long."

"But look, your worship," said Sancho, "those are not giants but windmills, and what seem to be their arms are the sails that, turned by the wind, make the millstone go."

"It is easy to see," replied Don Quixote, "that thou art not used to this business of adventures. Those are giants; and if thou art afraid, away with thee and betake thyself to prayer while I engage them in fierce and unequal combat."

So saying, he spurred on his steed Rocinante, paying no attention to Sancho's cries warning him that most certainly they were windmills and not giants he was going to attack. He was so positive they were giants that he neither heard the cries of Sancho nor saw what they were, but shouted, "Fly not, cowards and vile beings, for it is a single knight that attacks you."

At this moment a slight breeze sprang up, and the great sails began to move. Seeing this, Don Quixote exclaimed, "Though ye flourish more arms than the giant Briareus, ye have to reckon with me."

So saying, and commending himself with all his heart to his lady Dulcinea, imploring her to support him in such a peril, with his lance at rest and covered by his shield, he charged at Rocinante's fullest gallop and fell upon the first mill that stood in front of him. But as he drove his lance-point into the sail, the wind whirled it round with such force that it shivered the lance to pieces, sweeping with it horse and rider, who went rolling over on the plain in a sorry condition.

Sancho hastened to his assistance as fast as his ass could go, and when he came up found the knight unable to move, so great was the shock with which he and Rocinante had fallen.

Briareus: mythological giant with a hundred arms and fifty heads
imploring: asking earnestly; begging

"God bless me!" said Sancho, "did I not tell your worship that they were only windmills? No one could have made any mistake about it but one who had something of the same kind in his head."

"Hush, friend Sancho," replied Don Quixote, "the fortunes of war are subject to constant change; and moreover, I think, and it is the truth, that the magician Frestón has turned these giants into mills in order to rob me of the glory of vanquishing them, such is the enmity he bears me. But in the end his wicked arts shall not prevail against my good sword."

"God order it as he may," said Sancho Panza, and helping his master to rise got him up again on Rocinante, whose shoulder was half out. And then, discussing their adventure, they followed the road to Puerto Lapice, for there, said Don Quixote, they could not fail to find adventures in abundance and variety, as it was a great thoroughfare. Still, he was much grieved at the loss of his lance, and saying so to his squire, he added, "From the first oak I see I mean to rend a branch, large and stout, with which I am determined and resolved to do such deeds that thou mayest deem thyself very fortunate in being found worthy to be an eyewitness of things that will with difficulty be believed."

"Be that as God will," said Sancho, "I believe it all as your worship says it; but straighten yourself a little, for you seem all on one side, maybe from the shaking of the fall."

"That is the truth," said Don Quixote, "and if I make no complaint of the pain it is because knights-errant are not permitted to complain of any wounds."

"If so," said Sancho, "I have nothing to say; but God knows I would rather your worship complained when anything ailed you. For my part, I confess I must complain, however small the ache may be; unless indeed this rule about not complaining extends to the squires of knights-errant also."

Don Quixote could not help laughing at his squire's simplicity, and he assured him he might complain whenever and however he chose, just as he liked, for, so far, he had never read of anything to the contrary in the order of knighthood.

Sancho pointed out that it was dinner-time, to which his master answered that he wanted nothing himself just then, but that Sancho might eat when he had a mind. With this permission Sancho settled himself as comfortably as he could on his beast, and taking from his saddlebags the provisions he had stowed away in them, he jogged along behind his master munching deliberately, and from time to time taking a long swig from the wine skin. And while he went on in this way, gulping down draught after draught, he never gave a thought to any of the promises his master had made him, nor did he consider it as any hardship but rather as fine sport to go in quest of adventures, however dangerous they might be.

---

draught: large swallow

LOVE AND BEAUTY

SHE WALKS IN BEAUTY

George Gordon, Lord Byron

In his time, Lord Byron (1788–1824) was known the world over as a poet and a celebrity. This poem, written in 1814, is characteristic of the passionate feeling that often marked Byron's poetry. The images of light and dark interplay to create a memorable celebration of the beauty of the speaker's beloved.

She walks in beauty, like the night
   Of cloudless climes and starry skies;
And all that's best of dark and bright
   Meet in her aspect and her eyes:
Thus mellowed to that tender light   5
   Which heaven to gaudy day denies.

One shade the more, one ray the less,
   Had half impaired the nameless grace
Which waves in every raven tress,
   Or softly lightens o'er her face;   10
Where thoughts serenely sweet express
   How pure, how dear their dwelling place.

---

climes: climates
aspect: face; appearance
gaudy: tacky; showy
raven: black
tress: lock or curl of hair
serenely: calmly

And on that cheek, and o'er that brow,
    So soft, so calm, yet eloquent,
The smiles that win, the tints that glow,   15
    But tell of days in goodness spent,
A mind at peace with all below,
    A heart whose love is innocent!

---

eloquent: powerfully expressive

Sonnet 43

Elizabeth Barrett Browning

Elizabeth Barrett Browning (1806–1861) wrote this sonnet as part of her collection, Sonnets from the Portuguese. *Published in 1850, the compilation of 44 sonnets is a record of the courtship between Elizabeth and her future husband and fellow poet Robert Browning.*

How do I love thee? Let me count the ways.
I love thee to the depth and breadth and height
My soul can reach, when feeling out of sight
For the ends of Being and ideal Grace.
I love thee to the level of everyday's   5
Most quiet need, by sun and candle-light.
I love thee freely, as men strive for Right;
I love thee purely, as they turn from Praise.
I love thee with a passion put to use
In my old griefs, and with my childhood's faith.   10
I love thee with a love I seemed to lose
With my lost saints,—I love thee with the breath,
Smiles, tears, of all my life!—and, if God choose,
I shall but love thee better after death.

A Red, Red Rose

Robert Burns

Robert Burns (1759–1796) is today celebrated as the national poet of Scotland. Much of Burns's work is infused with words and phrases drawn from the Scottish language and dialect.

O my Luve's like a red, red rose,
    That's newly sprung in June;
O my Luve's like the melodie
    That's sweetly played in tune.

As fair art thou, my bonie lass,   5
    So deep in luve am I;
And I will love thee still, my Dear,
    Till a' the seas gang dry.

Till a' the seas gang dry, my Dear,
    And the rocks melt wi' the sun: 10
O I will love thee still, my Dear,
    While the sands o' life shall run.

And fare thee weel, my only Luve!
    And fare thee weel, a while!
And I will come again, my Luve,   15
    Tho' it were ten thousand mile!

---

luve's: love is
my bonie lass: my beautiful girl
gang: go
weel: well

THREE SONNETS

William Shakespeare

Sonnets are 14-line poems written with a specific meter and rhyme scheme. William Shakespeare (1564–1616) wrote more than 150 sonnets, most of which were first published in 1609, although their dates of composition are unknown. Many of Shakespeare's sonnets are commentaries on love. In these three sonnets, the poet celebrates love by describing how the thought of a beloved friend can cheer him when he is sad (Sonnet 30); compares his poetic work in honor of a beloved to other physical monuments (Sonnet 55); and extols the value, power, and endurance of true love (Sonnet 116).

SONNET 30

When to the sessions of sweet silent thought
I summon up remembrance of things past,
I sigh the lack of many a thing I sought,
And with old woes new wail my dear time's waste;
Then can I drown an eye, unused to flow,   5
For precious friends hid in death's dateless night,
And weep afresh love's long since cancelled woe,
And moan th' expense of many a vanished sight.
Then can I grieve at grievances foregone,
And heavily from woe to woe tell o'er   10
The sad account of fore-bemoanèd moan,
Which I new pay, as if not paid before.
    But if the while I think on thee, dear friend,
    All losses are restored and sorrows end.

sought: looked for; wanted
foregone: in the past

SONNET 55

Not marble, nor the gilded monuments
Of princes shall outlive this pow'rful rhyme;
But you shall shine more bright in these contents
Than unswept stone, besmeared with sluttish time.
When wasteful war shall statues overturn,   5
And broils root out the work of masonry,
Nor Mars his sword nor war's quick fire shall burn
The living record of your memory:
'Gainst death and all oblivious enmity
Shall you pace forth; your praise shall still find room   10
Even in the eyes of all posterity
That wear this world out to the ending doom.
    So till the judgment that yourself arise,
    You live in this, and dwell in lovers' eyes.

---

gilded: made from or coated with gold
besmeared: marred; stained
sluttish: untidy or sloppy
broils: clashes; fights
masonry: brickwork
Mars: in Roman mythology, the god of war
oblivious: ignorant; unknowing
enmity: hatred
posterity: future generations

49

Sonnet 116

Let me not to the marriage of true minds
Admit impediments; love is not love
Which alters when it alteration finds
Or bends with the remover to remove.
O, no, it is an ever-fixèd mark   5
That looks on tempests and is never shaken;
It is the star to every wand'ring bark,
Whose worth's unknown, although his height be taken.
Love's not Time's fool, though rosy lips and cheeks
Within his bending sickle's compass come;   10
Love alters not with his brief hours and weeks,
But bears it out even to the edge of doom.
    If this be error, and upon me proved,
    I never writ, nor no man ever loved.

---

impediments: hindrances
tempests: storms
bark: ship; boat
sickle: a tool with a curved blade, used to harvest grains
writ: wrote

SONG OF SOLOMON
CHAPTER 2

from the King James Bible

Song of Solomon, also known as the Song of Songs, is one of the shortest books in the Hebrew Bible or Old Testament. Its authorship is often attributed to Solomon, a king of ancient Israel and son of King David. This chapter focuses on the love that exists between a woman and a man.

1   I am the rose of Sharon, and the lily of the valleys.
2   As the lily among thorns, so is my love among the daughters.
3   As the apple tree among the trees of the wood, so is my beloved among the sons. I sat down under his shadow with great delight, and his fruit was sweet to my taste.
4   He brought me to the banqueting house, and his banner over me was love.
5   Stay me with flagons, comfort me with apples: for I am sick of love.
6   His left hand is under my head, and his right hand doth embrace me.
7   I charge you, O ye daughters of Jerusalem, by the roes, and by the hinds of the field, that ye stir not up, nor awake my love, till he please.
8   The voice of my beloved! behold, he cometh leaping upon the mountains, skipping upon the hills.

---

rose of Sharon: a flowering plant native to the Plain of Sharon, on the western coast of Israel
flagons: pitchers for holding liquid refreshments
roes: male deer or gazelles
hinds of the field: does or female deer

9   My beloved is like a roe or a young hart: behold, he standeth behind our wall, he looketh forth at the windows, shewing himself through the lattice.

10 My beloved spake, and said unto me, Rise up, my love, my fair one, and come away.

11 For, lo, the winter is past, the rain is over and gone;

12 The flowers appear on the earth; the time of the singing of birds is come, and the voice of the turtle is heard in our land;

13 The fig tree putteth forth her green figs, and the vines with the tender grape give a good smell. Arise, my love, my fair one, and come away.

---

hart: a stag or male deer
shewing: showing
lattice: strips of wood organized in a crisscross pattern
spake: spoke

THE NATURAL WORLD

ODES TO THE SEASONS

William Blake

Both a poet and a visual artist, William Blake (1757–1827) published many of his poems with vivid engravings of his own design. These odes are from his first collection of poetry, Poetical Sketches, *and are thought to have been written before the poet was 20 years old. Some of the imagery Blake evokes in these early works, such as imagining the seasons as mythical characters, is developed more fully in his more mature poetry.*

TO SPRING

O thou, with dewy locks, who lookest down
Thro' the clear windows of the morning, turn
Thine angel eyes upon our western isle,
Which in full choir hails thy approach, O Spring!

The hills tell each other, and the list'ning   5
Vallies hear; all our longing eyes are turned
Up to thy bright pavillions: issue forth,
And let thy holy feet visit our clime.

Come o'er the eastern hills, and let our winds
Kiss thy perfumed garments; let us taste   10
Thy morn and evening breath; scatter thy pearls
Upon our love-sick land that mourns for thee.

O deck her forth with thy fair fingers; pour
Thy soft kisses on her bosom; and put

---

vallies: valleys
pavillions: roofs; in this case, skies
clime: region

Thy golden crown upon her languish'd head,   15
Whose modest tresses were bound up for thee.

TO SUMMER

O thou who passest thro' our vallies in
Thy strength, curb thy fierce steeds, allay the heat
That flames from their large nostrils! thou, O Summer,
Oft pitched'st here thy golden tent, and oft
Beneath our oaks has slept, while we beheld   5
With joy thy ruddy limbs and flourishing hair.

Beneath our thickest shades we oft have heard
Thy voice, when noon upon his fervid car
Rode o'er the deep of heaven; beside our springs
Sit down, and in our mossy vallies, on   10
Some bank beside a river clear, throw thy
Silk draperies off, and rush into the stream:
Our vallies love the Summer in his pride.

Our bards are fam'd who strike the silver wire:
Our youth are bolder than the southern swains: 15
Our maidens fairer in the sprightly dance:
We lack not songs, nor instruments of joy,
Nor echoes sweet, nor waters clear as heaven,
Nor laurel wreaths against the sultry heat.

---

languish'd: weakened
modest: humble
tresses: locks; curls
steeds: horses
allay: calm; lighten or lessen
ruddy: red
fervid: hot
fervid car: burning carriage, a reference to the heat of the
    noontime sun
bards: traveling poets or singers
fam'd: famed; famous
swains: young men who are admirers or lovers of women
sprightly: energetic
sultry: stifling

TO AUTUMN

O Autumn, laden with fruit, and stained
With the blood of the grape, pass not, but sit
Beneath my shady roof; there thou may'st rest,
And tune thy jolly voice to my fresh pipe,
And all the daughters of the year shall dance!   5
Sing now the lusty song of fruits and flowers.

"The narrow bud opens her beauties to
The sun, and love runs in her thrilling veins;
Blossoms hang round the brows of morning, and
Flourish down the bright cheek of modest eve,   10
Till clustr'ing Summer breaks forth into singing,
And feather'd clouds strew flowers round her head.

"The spirits of the air live on the smells
Of fruit; and joy, with pinions light, roves round
The gardens, or sits singing in the trees."   15
Thus sang the jolly Autumn as he sat;
Then rose, girded himself, and o'er the bleak
Hills fled from our sight; but left his golden load.

---

laden: filled or loaded; burdened
eve: evening
pinions: wings
roves: wanders
girded: prepared for action
bleak: desolate; cheerless

TO WINTER

"O Winter! bar thine adamantine doors:
The north is thine; there hast thou built thy dark
Deep-founded habitation. Shake not thy roofs,
Nor bend thy pillars with thine iron car."

He hears me not, but o'er the yawning deep   5
Rides heavy; his storms are unchain'd, sheathed
In ribbed steel; I dare not lift mine eyes,
For he hath rear'd his sceptre o'er the world.

Lo! now the direful monster, whose skin clings
To his strong bones, strides o'er the groaning rocks: 10
He withers all in silence, and his hand
Unclothes the earth, and freezes up frail life.

He takes his seat upon the cliffs; the mariner
Cries in vain. Poor little wretch! that deal'st
With storms, till heaven smiles, and the monster   15
Is driv'n yelling to his caves beneath mount Hecla.

---

adamantine: unbreakable
habitation: home
sheathed: encased
sceptre: a staff symbolizing power
direful: fearful
withers: shrinks; enfeebles
frail: weak
wretch: a miserable person
mount Hecla: an Icelandic volcano that was believed to be a
    gateway to hell

I WANDERED LONELY AS A CLOUD

William Wordsworth

William Wordsworth (1770–1850), one of the founders of the Romantic movement in poetry in England, often found inspiration in nature. This well-known poem is sometimes called "The Daffodils."

I wandered lonely as a cloud
That floats on high o'er vales and hills,
When all at once I saw a crowd,
A host, of golden daffodils;
Beside the lake, beneath the trees,   5
Fluttering and dancing in the breeze.

Continuous as the stars that shine
And twinkle on the milky way,
They stretched in never-ending line
Along the margin of a bay: 10
Ten thousand saw I at a glance,
Tossing their heads in sprightly dance.

The waves beside them danced; but they
Out-did the sparkling waves in glee:
A poet could not but be gay,   15
In such a jocund company:
I gazed—and gazed—but little thought
What wealth the show to me had brought:

---

vales: valleys
margin: edge; shore
gay: happy; jolly
jocund: jovial; happy

For oft, when on my couch I lie
In vacant or in pensive mood,   20
They flash upon that inward eye
Which is the bliss of solitude;
And then my heart with pleasure fills,
And dances with the daffodils.

pensive: thoughtful

LINES WRITTEN IN EARLY SPRING

William Wordsworth

This poem first appeared in a 1798 volume titled Lyrical Ballads, *a book with works by both Wordsworth and his friend and fellow Romantic poet, Samuel Taylor Coleridge.*

I heard a thousand blended notes,
While in a grove I sate reclined,
In that sweet mood when pleasant thoughts
Bring sad thoughts to the mind.

To her fair works did Nature link   5
The human soul that through me ran;
And much it grieved my heart to think
What man has made of man.

Through primrose tufts, in that green bower,
The periwinkle trailed its wreaths;   10
And 'tis my faith that every flower
Enjoys the air it breathes.

The birds around me hopped and played,
Their thoughts I cannot measure—
But the least motion which they made,   15
It seemed a thrill of pleasure.

---

grove: a wooded area
sate: sat
grieved: saddened
primrose tufts: bunches of a plant with white, red, or yellow
    flowers
bower: a place enclosed by tree branches or vines
periwinkle: a plant with blue flowers

The budding twigs spread our their fan,
To catch the breezy air;
And I must think, do all I can,
That there was pleasure there. 20

If this belief from heaven be sent,
If such be Nature's holy plan,
Have I not reason to lament
What man has made of man?

lament: mourn; be sad over

TO A BUTTERFLY

William Wordsworth

*Written in 1802, this poem is another example of the inspiration
Wordsworth drew from the natural world.*

I've watched you now a full half-hour,
Self-poised upon that yellow flower;
And, little Butterfly! indeed
I know not if you sleep or feed.
How motionless!—not frozen seas   5
More motionless! and then
What joy awaits you, when the breeze
Hath found you out among the trees,
And calls you forth again!

This plot of orchard-ground is ours;   10
My trees they are, my Sister's flowers;
Here rest your wings when they are weary;
Here lodge as in a sanctuary!
Come often to us, fear no wrong;
Sit near us on the bough!   15
We'll talk of sunshine and of song,
And summer days, when we were young;
Sweet childish days, that were as long
As twenty days are now.

---

plot: area
sanctuary: a shelter; a place of total safety

Sonnet to the River Otter

Samuel Taylor Coleridge

With his friend and fellow poet William Wordsworth, Samuel Taylor Coleridge (1772–1834) was one of the founders of the Romantic movement in English poetry. In this work, the poet fondly recalls the time he spent as a child near the River Otter, a waterway near Exeter, England, that flows into the English Channel.

Dear native Brook! wild Streamlet of the West!
   How many various-fated years have past,
   What happy and what mournful hours, since last
I skimm'd the smooth thin stone along thy breast,
Numbering its light leaps! yet so deep imprest   5
Sink the sweet scenes of childhood, that mine eyes
   I never shut amid the sunny ray,
But straight with all their tints thy waters rise,
   Thy crossing plank, thy marge with willows grey,
And bedded sand that vein'd with various dyes   10
Gleam'd through thy bright transparence! On my way,
   Visions of Childhood! oft have ye beguil'd
Lone manhood's cares, yet waking fondest sighs:
   Ah! That once more I were a careless Child!

---

brook: stream; small river
tints: colors; shades
marge: edge; in this case, the bank of the stream
vein'd: shot through with color
transparence: clearness
beguil'd: charmed
lone: lonely

Lines to a Beautiful Spring in a Village

Samuel Taylor Coleridge

First published in 1796, this poem demonstrates the Romantic instinct to use classical references and allusions to address the beauty of the natural world.

Once more! sweet Stream! with slow foot wandering
   near,
I bless thy milky waters cold and clear.
Escap'd the flashing of the noontide hours,
With one fresh garland of Pierian flowers
(Ere from thy zephyr-haunted brink I turn)   5
My languid hand shall wreath thy mossy urn.
For not through pathless grove with murmur rude
Thou soothest the sad wood-nymph, Solitude;
Nor thine unseen in cavern depths to well,
The Hermit-fountain of some dripping cell!   10

Pride of the Vale! thy useful streams supply
The scatter'd cots and peaceful hamlet nigh.
The elfin tribe around thy friendly banks

---

garland: a wreath or intertwined string of flowers or vines
Pierian: relating to a region of ancient Macedonia where Mount
    Pierus stood; Mount Pierus was home to the Muses, who were
    the ancient Greek goddesses of poetry
zephyr: a soft breeze
languid: relaxed
grove: wooded area
soothest: calm
vale: valley
cots: places to sleep
hamlet: village
nigh: near

With infant uproar and soul-soothing pranks,
Releas'd from school, their little hearts at rest,   15
Launch paper navies on thy waveless breast.
The rustic here at eve with pensive look
Whistling lorn ditties leans upon his crook,
Or, starting, pauses with hope-mingled dread
To list the much-lov'd maid's accustom'd tread: 20
She, vainly mindful of her dame's command,
Loiters, the long-fill'd pitcher in her hand.

Unboastful Stream! thy fount with pebbled falls
The faded form of past delight recalls,
What time the morning sun of Hope arose,   25
And all was joy; save when another's woes
A transient gloom upon my soul imprest,
Like passing clouds impictur'd on thy breast.
Life's current then ran sparkling to the noon,
Or silvery stole beneath the pensive Moon: 30
Ah! now it works rude brakes and thorns among,
Or o'er the rough rock bursts and foams along!

_____

navies: ships
rustic: country person
pensive: thoughtful
lorn ditties: sad songs
crook: cane
list: listen to
tread: the sound of a person's walk
loiters: waits; delays
fount: fountain
transient: passing; temporary
impictur'd: reflected

THE CLOUD

Percy Bysshe Shelley

In his time, Percy Bysshe Shelley (1792–1822) was a controversial figure, both for his radical politics and his unconventional personal life. While spending time in Italy, Shelley shifted his attention from political action to focus on his art. He eventually published his 1820 collection Prometheus Unbound, *which contains this poem. The speaker is a cloud.*

I bring fresh showers for the thirsting flowers,
    From the seas and the streams;
I bear light shade for the leaves when laid
    In their noonday dreams.
From my wings are shaken the dews that waken   5
    The sweet buds every one,
When rocked to rest on their mother's breast,
    As she dances about the sun.
I wield the flail of the lashing hail,
    And whiten the green plains under;   10
And then again I dissolve it in rain,
    And laugh as I pass in thunder.

I sift the snow on the mountains below,
    And their great pines groan aghast;
And all the night 'tis my pillow white,   15
    While I sleep in the arms of the blast.
Sublime on the towers of my skiey bowers,
    Lightning my pilot sits;

---

wield: command; have authority over
flail: an implement used to make strong, violent movements
lashing: pouring; falling quickly and violently
aghast: shocked with horror
sublime: magnificent
bowers: enclosed and peaceful areas

In a cavern under is fettered the thunder,
 It struggles and howls at fits;   20
Over earth and ocean, with gentle motion,
 This pilot is guiding me,
Lured by the love of the genii that move
 In the depths of the purple sea;
Over the rills, and the crags, and the hills,   25
 Over the lakes and the plains,
Wherever he dream, under mountain or stream,
 The Spirit he loves remains;
And I all the while bask in Heaven's blue smile,
 Whilst he is dissolving in rains.   30

The sanguine Sunrise, with his meteor eyes,
 And his burning plumes outspread,
Leaps on the back of my sailing rack,
 When the morning star shines dead;
As on the jag of a mountain crag,   35
 Which an earthquake rocks and swings,
An eagle alit one moment may sit
 In the light of its golden wings.
And when Sunset may breathe, from the lit sea beneath,
 Its ardours of rest and of love,   40
And the crimson pall of eve may fall
 From the depth of Heaven above,
With wings folded I rest, on mine aëry nest,
 As still as a brooding dove.

---

fettered: chained; shackled
genii: magical spirits
rills: small streams
crags: cliffs
bask: relax in warmth
sanguine: optimistic; hopeful
plumes: things that resemble feathers
alit: landed
ardours: intense feelings
crimson pall: a curtain of deep red
aëry: lofty; high
brooding dove: a dove sitting on its eggs in a nest

That orbed maiden with white fire laden,   45
    Whom mortals call the Moon,
Glides glimmering o'er my fleece-like floor,
    By the midnight breezes strewn;
And wherever the beat of her unseen feet,
    Which only the angels hear,   50
May have broken the woof of my tent's thin roof,
    The stars peep behind her and peer;
And I laugh to see them whirl and flee,
    Like a swarm of golden bees,
When I widen the rent in my wind-built tent,   55
    Till the calm rivers, lakes, and seas,
Like strips of the sky fallen through me on high,
    Are each paved with the moon and these.

I bind the Sun's throne with a burning zone,
    And the Moon's with a girdle of pearl;   60
The volcanoes are dim, and the stars reel and swim,
    When the whirlwinds my banner unfurl.
From cape to cape, with a bridge-like shape,
    Over a torrent sea,
Sunbeam-proof, I hang like a roof,—   65
    The mountains its columns be.
The triumphal arch through which I march
    With hurricane, fire, and snow,
When the Powers of the air are chained to my chair,
    Is the million-coloured bow;   70
The sphere-fire above its soft colours wove,
    While the moist Earth was laughing below.

---

orbed: round
laden: filled or totally covered in
strewn: scattered
woof: horizontal strands woven to create a fabric
rent: ripped opening; tear
girdle: a belt or other instrument of restraint
torrent: surge; flood

I am the daughter of Earth and Water,
    And the nursling of the Sky,
I pass through the pores of the ocean and shores;   75
    I change, but I cannot die.
For after the rain when with never a stain
    The pavilion of Heaven is bare,
And the winds and sunbeams with their convex gleams
    Build up the blue dome of air,   80
I silently laugh at my own cenotaph,
    And out of the caverns of rain,
Like a child from the womb, like a ghost from the tomb,
    I arise and unbuild it again.

---

nursling: something nurtured or tenderly cared for
pavilion: a large tent
convex: curved
cenotaph: a tomb built for someone whose remains are elsewhere

THE HUMAN SEASONS

John Keats

John Keats (1795–1821) died of tuberculosis at the age of 25. In his short career, he produced a lasting and influential body of poetry that expresses the Romantic cultivation of deep and intense feeling. This sonnet likens the stages of a human lifetime to the four seasons of the year.

Four seasons fill the measure of the year;
    There are four seasons in the mind of man:
He has his lusty Spring, when fancy clear
    Takes in all beauty with an easy span:
He has his Summer, when luxuriously   5
    Spring's honied cud of youthful thought he loves
To ruminate, and by such dreaming nigh
    His nearest unto heaven: quiet coves
His soul has in its Autumn, when his wings
    He furleth close; contented so to look   10
On mists in idleness—to let fair things
    Pass by unheeded as a threshold brook.
He has his Winter too of pale misfortune,
Or else he would forgo his mortal nature.

---

lusty: healthy; robust
fancy: imagination or interpretation
span: an encompassing reach
honied: sweet, as though covered in honey
cud: a piece of food that is chewed again and again
ruminate: ponder; reflect on
nigh: near; just about
coves: small caves or inlets
furleth: rolls up
unheeded: unnoticed
forgo: give up

SHERLOCK HOLMES
MYSTERIES

THE ADVENTURE OF THE SPECKLED BAND

Sir Arthur Conan Doyle

Sherlock Holmes, the greatest and probably most famous fictional detective in literature, is the main character of 4 novels and more than 50 short stories by Sir Arthur Conan Doyle (1859–1930). Most of the stories about Sherlock Holmes are narrated by his faithful companion, Dr. John H. Watson. In the following tale, Watson relates the story of a case in which Holmes is hired by a woman who suspects that her sister's death was no accident, and that her own life might be in danger.

On glancing over my notes of the seventy odd cases in which I have during the last eight years studied the methods of my friend Sherlock Holmes, I find many tragic, some comic, a large number merely strange, but none commonplace; for working as he did rather for the love of his art than for the acquirement of wealth, he refused to associate himself with any investigation which did not tend towards the unusual, and even the fantastic. Of all these varied cases, however, I cannot recall any which presented more singular features than that which was associated with the well-known Surrey family of the Roylotts of Stoke Moran. The events in question occurred in the early days of my association with Holmes, when we were sharing rooms as bachelors in Baker Street. It is possible that I might have placed them upon record before, but a promise of secrecy was made at the time, for which I have only been freed during the last month by the untimely death of the lady to whom the pledge was given. It is perhaps as well that the facts should now come to light, for I have reasons to know that there are widespread rumours as to the death of Dr. Grimesby Roylott which tend to make the matter even more terrible than the truth.

---

singular: unique; unusual
Surrey: a county in southeast England
Baker Street: Holmes's home in London is an apartment at 221B Baker Street

It was early in April in the year '83 that I woke one morning to find Sherlock Holmes standing, fully dressed, by side of my bed. He was a late riser, as a rule, and as the clock on the mantelpiece showed me that it was only a quarter-past seven, I blinked up at him in some surprise, and perhaps just a little resentment, for I was myself regular in my habits.

"Very sorry to wake you up, Watson," said he, "but it's the common lot this morning. Mrs. Hudson has been waked up, she retorted upon me, and I on you."

"What is it, then—a fire?"

"No; a client. It seems that a young lady has arrived in a considerable state of excitement, who insists upon seeing me. She is waiting now in the sitting-room. Now, when young ladies wander about the metropolis at this hour of the morning, and knock sleepy people up out of their beds, I presume that it is something very pressing which they have to communicate. Should it prove to be an interesting case, you would, I am sure, wish to follow it from the outset. I thought, at any rate, that I should call you and give you the chance."

"My dear fellow, I would not miss it for anything."

I had no keener pleasure than in following Holmes in his professional investigations, and in admiring the rapid deductions, as swift as intuitions, and yet always founded on a logical basis, with which he unravelled the problems which were submitted to him. I rapidly threw on my clothes and was ready in a few minutes to accompany my friend down to the sitting-room. A lady dressed in black and heavily veiled, who had been sitting in the window, rose as we entered.

"Good-morning, madam," said Holmes cheerily. "My name is Sherlock Holmes. This is my intimate friend and associate, Dr. Watson, before whom you can speak as freely as before myself. Ha! I am glad to see that Mrs. Hudson has had the good sense to light the fire. Pray draw up to it, and I shall order you a cup of hot coffee, for I observe that you are shivering."

---

the common lot: the fate of everyone
retorted: retaliated
keener: sharper; greater
deductions: inferences made through the use of logic

"It is not cold which makes me shiver," said the woman in a low voice, changing her seat as requested.

"What, then?"

"It is fear, Mr. Holmes. It is terror." She raised her veil as she spoke, and we could see that she was indeed in a pitiable state of agitation, her face all drawn and gray, with restless, frightened eyes, like those of some hunted animal. Her features and figure were those of a woman of thirty, but her hair was shot with premature gray, and her expression was weary and haggard. Sherlock Holmes ran her over with one of his quick, all-comprehensive glances.

"You must not fear," said he soothingly, bending forward and patting her forearm. "We shall soon set matters right, I have no doubt. You have come in by train this morning, I see."

"You know me, then?"

"No, but I observe the second half of a return ticket in the palm of your left glove. You must have started early, and yet you had a good drive in a dog-cart, along heavy roads, before you reached the station."

The lady gave a violent start and stared in bewilderment at my companion.

"There is no mystery, my dear madam," said he, smiling. "The left arm of your jacket is spattered with mud in no less than seven places. The marks are perfectly fresh. There is no vehicle save a dog-cart which throws up mud in that way, and then only when you sit on the left-hand side of the driver."

"Whatever your reasons may be, you are perfectly correct," said she. "I started from home before six, reached Leatherhead at twenty past, and came in by the first train to Waterloo. Sir, I can stand this strain no longer; I shall go mad if it continues. I have no one to turn to—none, save only one, who cares for me, and he, poor fellow, can be of little aid. I have heard of you, Mr. Holmes; I have heard of you from Mrs. Farintosh, whom you helped in the hour of her sore need. It was from her that I had your address. Oh, sir, do you not

haggard: worn down
return ticket: round-trip ticket
Leatherhead: a large town in Surrey, England
Waterloo: Waterloo Station, a main train station in London

think that you could help me, too, and at least throw a little light through the dense darkness which surrounds me? At present it is out of my power to reward you for your services, but in a month or six weeks I shall be married, with the control of my own income, and then at least you shall not find me ungrateful."

Holmes turned to his desk and, unlocking it, drew out a small case-book, which he consulted.

"Farintosh," said he. "Ah yes, I recall the case; it was concerned with an opal tiara. I think it was before your time, Watson. I can only say, madam, that I shall be happy to devote the same care to your case as I did to that of your friend. As to reward, my profession is its own reward; but you are at liberty to defray whatever expenses I may be put to, at the time which suits you best. And now I beg that you will lay before us everything that may help us in forming an opinion upon the matter."

"Alas!" replied our visitor, "the very horror of my situation lies in the fact that my fears are so vague, and my suspicions depend so entirely upon small points, which might seem trivial to another, that even he to whom of all others I have a right to look for help and advice looks upon all that I tell him about it as the fancies of a nervous woman. He does not say so, but I can read it from his soothing answers and averted eyes. But I have heard, Mr. Holmes, that you can see deeply into the manifold wickedness of the human heart. You may advise me how to walk amid the dangers which encompass me."

"I am all attention, madam."

"My name is Helen Stoner, and I am living with my stepfather, who is the last survivor of one of the oldest Saxon families in England, the Roylotts of Stoke Moran, on the western border of Surrey."

Holmes nodded his head. "The name is familiar to me," said he.

---

tiara: crown
defray: settle; pay
averted: turned away; turned aside
manifold: multiple; diverse
encompass: surround

"The family was at one time among the richest in England, and the estates extended over the borders into Berkshire in the north, and Hampshire in the west. In the last century, however, four successive heirs were of a dissolute and wasteful disposition, and the family ruin was eventually completed by a gambler in the days of the Regency. Nothing was left save a few acres of ground, and the two-hundred-year-old house, which is itself crushed under a heavy mortgage. The last squire dragged out his existence there, living the horrible life of an aristocratic pauper; but his only son, my stepfather, seeing that he must adapt himself to the new conditions, obtained an advance from a relative, which enabled him to take a medical degree and went out to Calcutta, where, by his professional skill and his force of character, he established a large practice. In a fit of anger, however, caused by some robberies which had been perpetrated in the house, he beat his native butler to death and narrowly escaped a capital sentence. As it was, he suffered a long term of imprisonment and afterwards returned to England a morose and disappointed man.

"When Dr. Roylott was in India he married my mother, Mrs. Stoner, the young widow of Major-General Stoner, of the Bengal Artillery. My sister Julia and I were twins, and we were only two years old at the time of my mother's remarriage. She had a considerable sum of money—not less than £1000 a year—and this she bequeathed to Dr. Roylott entirely while we resided with him, with a provision that a certain annual sum should be allowed to each of us in the event of our marriage. Shortly after our return to England

---

Berkshire; Hampshire: counties bordering Surrey in southeast England
dissolute: immoral
disposition: character; inclination
the Regency: period from 1811 to 1820, when the Prince of Wales was regent of
    England due to King George III's insanity
squire: landowner
pauper: poor person
Calcutta: a large city in India
perpetrated: committed
capital sentence: death sentence
morose: miserable
£: symbol for pounds, the basic unit of money in Great Britain
bequeathed: gave
provision: condition

my mother died—she was killed eight years ago in a railway accident near Crewe. Dr. Roylott then abandoned his attempts to establish himself in practice in London and took us to live with him in the old ancestral house at Stoke Moran. The money which my mother had left was enough for our wants, and there seemed to be no obstacle to our happiness.

"But a terrible change came over our stepfather about this time. Instead of making friends and exchanging visits with our neighbours, who had at first been overjoyed to see a Roylott of Stoke Moran back in the old family seat, he shut himself up in his house and seldom came out save to indulge in ferocious quarrels with whoever might cross his path. Violence of temper approaching to mania has been hereditary in the men of the family, and in my stepfather's case it had, I believe, been intensified by his long residence in the tropics. A series of disgraceful brawls took place, two of which ended in the police-court, until at last he became the terror of the village, and the folks would fly at his approach, for he is a man of immense strength, and absolutely uncontrollable in his anger.

"Last week he hurled the local blacksmith over a parapet into a stream, and it was only by paying over all the money which I could gather together that I was able to avert another public exposure. He had no friends at all save the wandering gypsies, and he would give these vagabonds leave to encamp upon the few acres of bramblecovered land which represent the family estate, and would accept in return the hospitality of their tents, wandering away with them sometimes for weeks on end. He has a passion also for Indian animals, which are sent over to him by a correspondent, and he has at this moment a cheetah and a baboon, which wander freely over his grounds and are feared by the villagers almost as much as their master.

"You can imagine from what I say that my poor sister Julia and I had no great pleasure in our lives. No servant would stay with us,

Crewe: a large town in Cheshire, northwest England
indulge: engage
parapet: a low wall
exposure: scandal
vagabonds: tramps
leave: permission

and for a long time we did all the work of the house. She was but thirty at the time of her death, and yet her hair had already begun to whiten, even as mine has."

"Your sister is dead, then?"

"She died just two years ago, and it is of her death that I wish to speak to you. You can understand that, living the life which I have described, we were little likely to see anyone of our own age and position. We had, however, an aunt, my mother's maiden sister, Miss Honoria Westphail, who lives near Harrow, and we were occasionally allowed to pay short visits at this lady's house. Julia went there at Christmas two years ago, and met there a half-pay major of marines, to whom she became engaged. My stepfather learned of the engagement when my sister returned and offered no objection to the marriage; but within a fortnight of the day which had been fixed for the wedding, the terrible event occurred which has deprived me of my only companion."

Sherlock Holmes had been leaning back in his chair with his eyes closed and his head sunk in a cushion, but he half opened his lids now and glanced across at his visitor.

"Pray be precise as to details," said he.

"It is easy for me to be so, for every event of that dreadful time is seared into my memory. The manorhouse is, as I have already said, very old, and only one wing is now inhabited. The bedrooms in this wing are on the ground floor, the sitting-rooms being in the central block of the buildings. Of these bedrooms the first is Dr. Roylott's, the second my sister's, and the third my own. There is no communication between them, but they all open out into the same corridor. Do I make myself plain?"

"Perfectly so."

"The windows of the three rooms open out upon the lawn. That fatal night Dr. Roylott had gone to his room early, though we knew that he had not retired to rest, for my sister was troubled by the smell of the strong Indian cigars which it was his custom to smoke. She left her room, therefore, and came into mine, where she sat for

---

Harrow: an area of London
fortnight: two weeks
seared: burned

78

some time, chatting about her approaching wedding. At eleven o'clock she rose to leave me, but she paused at the door and looked back.

"'Tell me, Helen,' said she, 'have you ever heard anyone whistle in the dead of the night?'

"'Never,' said I.

"'I suppose that you could not possibly whistle, yourself, in your sleep?'

"'Certainly not. But why?'

"'Because during the last few nights I have always, about three in the morning, heard a low, clear whistle. I am a light sleeper, and it has awakened me. I cannot tell where it came from—perhaps from the next room, perhaps from the lawn. I thought that I would just ask you whether you had heard it.'

"'No, I have not. It must be those wretched gypsies in the plantation.'

"'Very likely. And yet if it were on the lawn, I wonder that you did not hear it also.'

"'Ah, but I sleep more heavily than you.'

"'Well, it is of no great consequence, at any rate.' She smiled back at me, closed my door, and a few moments later I heard her key turn in the lock."

"Indeed," said Holmes. "Was it your custom always to lock yourselves in at night?"

"Always."

"And why?"

"I think that I mentioned to you that the doctor kept a cheetah and a baboon. We had no feeling of security unless our doors were locked."

"Quite so. Pray proceed with your statement."

"I could not sleep that night. A vague feeling of impending misfortune impressed me. My sister and I, you will recollect, were twins, and you know how subtle are the links which bind two souls which are so closely allied. It was a wild night. The wind was howling outside, and the rain was beating and splashing against

---

impending: upcoming

the windows. Suddenly, amid all the hubbub of the gale, there burst forth the wild scream of a terrified woman. I knew that it was my sister's voice. I sprang from my bed, wrapped a shawl around me, and rushed into the corridor. As I opened my door I seemed to hear a low whistle, such as my sister described, and a few moments later a clanging sound, as if a mass of metal had fallen. As I ran down the passage, my sister's door was unlocked, and revolved slowly upon its hinges. I stared at it horrorstricken, not knowing what was about to issue from it. By the light of the corridor-lamp I saw my sister appear at the opening, her face blanched with terror, her hands groping for help, her whole figure swaying to and fro like that of a drunkard. I ran to her and threw my arms round her, but at that moment her knees seemed to give way and she fell to the ground. She writhed as one who is in terrible pain, and her limbs were dreadfully convulsed. At first I thought that she had not recognized me, but as I bent over her she suddenly shrieked out in a voice which I shall never forget, 'Oh, my God! Helen! It was the band! The speckled band!' There was something else which she would fain have said, and she stabbed with her finger into the air in the direction of the doctor's room, but a fresh convulsion seized her and choked her words. I rushed out, calling loudly for my stepfather, and I met him hastening from his room in his dressing-gown. When he reached my sister's side she was unconscious, and though he poured brandy down her throat and sent for medical aid from the village, all efforts were in vain, for she slowly sank and died without having recovered her consciousness. Such was the dreadful end of my beloved sister."

"One moment," said Holmes; "are you sure about this whistle and metallic sound? Could you swear to it?"

"That was what the county coroner asked me at the inquiry. It is my strong impression that I heard it, and yet, among the crash of

gale: storm
horrorstricken: horrified
blanched: whitened
writhed: twisted
convulsed: shaken and twitching
speckled: dotted
fain: willingly

the gale and the creaking of an old house, I may possibly have been deceived."

"Was your sister dressed?"

"No, she was in her night-dress. In her right hand was found the charred stump of a match, and in her left a match-box."

"Showing that she had struck a light and looked about her when the alarm took place. That is important. And what conclusions did the coroner come to?"

"He investigated the case with great care, for Dr. Roylott's conduct had long been notorious in the county, but he was unable to find any satisfactory cause of death. My evidence showed that the door had been fastened upon the inner side, and the windows were blocked by old-fashioned shutters with broad iron bars, which were secured every night. The walls were carefully sounded, and were shown to be quite solid all round, and the flooring was also thoroughly examined with the same result. The chimney is wide, but is barred up by four large staples. It is certain, therefore, that my sister was quite alone when she met her end. Besides, there were no marks of any violence upon her."

"How about poison?"

"The doctors examined her for it, but without success."

"What do you think that this unfortunate lady died of, then?"

"It is my belief that she died of pure fear and nervous shock, though what it was that frightened her I cannot imagine."

"Were there gypsies in the plantation at the time?"

"Yes, there are nearly always some there."

"Ah, and what did you gather from this allusion to a band—a speckled band?"

"Sometimes I have thought that it was merely the wild talk of delirium, sometimes that it may have referred to some band of people, perhaps to these very gypsies in the plantation. I do not know whether the spotted handkerchiefs which so many of them wear over their heads might have suggested the strange adjective which she used."

Holmes shook his head like a man who is far from being satisfied.

---

delirium: mental confusion brought on by severe stress, sickness, or injury

"These are very deep waters," said he; "pray go on with your narrative."

"Two years have passed since then, and my life has been until lately lonelier than ever. A month ago, however, a dear friend, whom I have known for many years, has done me the honour to ask my hand in marriage. His name is Armitage—Percy Armitage—the second son of Mr. Armitage, of Crane Water, near Reading. My stepfather has offered no opposition to the match, and we are to be married in the course of the spring. Two days ago some repairs were started in the west wing of the building, and my bedroom wall has been pierced so that I have had to move into the chamber in which my sister died, and to sleep in the very bed in which she slept. Imagine, then, my thrill of terror when last night, as I lay awake, thinking over her terrible fate, I suddenly heard in the silence of the night the low whistle which had been the herald of her own death. I sprang up and lit the lamp, but nothing was to be seen in the room. I was too shaken to go to bed again, however, so I dressed, and as soon as it was daylight I slipped down, got a dogcart at the Crown Inn, which is opposite, and drove to Leatherhead, from whence I have come on this morning with the one object of seeing you and asking your advice."

"You have done wisely," said my friend. "But have you told me all?"

"Yes, all."

"Miss Roylott, you have not. You are screening your stepfather."

"Why, what do you mean?"

For answer Holmes pushed back the frill of black lace which fringed the hand that lay upon our visitor's knee. Five little livid spots, the marks of four fingers and a thumb, were printed upon the white wrist.

"You have been cruelly used," said Holmes.

The lady coloured deeply and covered over her injured wrist. "He is a hard man," she said, "and perhaps he hardly knows his own strength."

Reading: a large town west of London
herald: signal
screening: protecting
livid: bruised

There was a long silence, during which Holmes leaned his chin upon his hands and stared into the crackling fire.

"This is a very deep business," he said at last. "There are a thousand details which I should desire to know before I decide upon our course of action. Yet we have not a moment to lose. If we were to come to Stoke Moran today, would it be possible for us to see over these rooms without the knowledge of your stepfather?"

"As it happens, he spoke of coming into town today upon some most important business. It is probable that he will be away all day, and that there would be nothing to disturb you. We have a housekeeper now, but she is old and foolish, and I could easily get her out of the way."

"Excellent. You are not averse to this trip, Watson?"

"By no means."

"Then we shall both come. What are you going to do yourself?"

"I have one or two things which I would wish to do now that I am in town. But I shall return by the twelve o'clock train, so as to be there in time for your coming."

"And you may expect us early in the afternoon. I have myself some small business matters to attend to. Will you not wait and breakfast?"

"No, I must go. My heart is lightened already since I have confided my trouble to you. I shall look forward to seeing you again this afternoon." She dropped her thick black veil over her face and glided from the room.

"And what do you think of it all, Watson?" asked Sherlock Holmes, leaning back in his chair.

"It seems to me to be a most dark and sinister business."

"Dark enough and sinister enough."

"Yet if the lady is correct in saying that the flooring and walls are sound, and that the door, window, and chimney are impassable, then her sister must have been undoubtedly alone when she met her mysterious end."

---

averse to: opposed to
sinister: threatening evil or harm
impassable: impenetrable

"What becomes, then, of these nocturnal whistles, and what of the very peculiar words of the dying woman?'"

"I cannot think."

"When you combine the ideas of whistles at night, the presence of a band of gypsies who are on intimate terms with this old doctor, the fact that we have every reason to believe that the doctor has an interest in preventing his stepdaughter's marriage, the dying allusion to a band, and, finally, the fact that Miss Helen Stoner heard a metallic clang, which might have been caused by one of those metal bars that secured the shutters falling back into its place, I think that there is good ground to think that the mystery may be cleared along those lines."

"But what, then, did the gypsies do?"

"I cannot imagine."

"I see many objections to any such theory."

"And so do I. It is precisely for that reason that we are going to Stoke Moran this day. I want to see whether the objections are fatal, or if they may be explained away. But what in the name of the devil!"

The ejaculation had been drawn from my companion by the fact that our door had been suddenly dashed open, and that a huge man had framed himself in the aperture. His costume was a peculiar mixture of the professional and of the agricultural, having a black top-hat, a long frock-coat, and a pair of high gaiters, with a hunting-crop swinging in his hand. So tall was he that his hat actually brushed the cross bar of the doorway, and his breadth seemed to span it across from side to side. A large face, seared with a thousand wrinkles burned yellow with the sun, and marked with every evil passion, was turned from one to the other of us, while his deep-set, bile-shot eyes, and his high, thin, fleshless nose, gave him somewhat the resemblance of a fierce old bird of prey.

"Which of you is Holmes?" asked the apparition.

nocturnal: occurring at night
ejaculation: exclamation
aperture: opening; doorway
gaiters: boots
hunting-crop: a short whip
breadth: width

"My name, sir; but you have the advantage of me," said my companion quietly.

"I am Dr. Grimesby Roylott, of Stoke Moran."

"Indeed, Doctor," said Holmes blandly. "Pray take a seat."

"I will do nothing of the kind. My stepdaughter has been here. I have traced her. What has she been saying to you?"

"It is a little cold for the time of the year," said Holmes.

"What has she been saying to you?" screamed the old man furiously.

"But I have heard that the crocuses promise well," continued my companion imperturbably.

"Ha! You put me off, do you?" said our new visitor, taking a step forward and shaking his hunting-crop. "I know you, you scoundrel! I have heard of you before. You are Holmes, the meddler."

My friend smiled.

"Holmes, the busybody!"

His smile broadened.

"Holmes, the Scotland Yard Jack-in-office!"

Holmes chuckled heartily. "Your conversation is most entertaining," said he. "When you go out close the door, for there is a decided draught."

"I will go when I have said my say. Don't you dare meddle with my affairs. I know that Miss Stoner has been here. I traced her! I am a dangerous man to fall foul of! See here." He stepped swiftly forward, seized the poker, and bent it into a curve with his huge brown hands.

"See that you keep yourself out of my grip," he snarled, and hurling the twisted poker into the fireplace he strode out of the room.

"He seems a very amiable person," said Holmes, laughing. "I am not quite so bulky, but if he had remained I might have shown him that my grip was not much more feeble than his own." As

crocuses: flowering plants
imperturbably: without being disturbed
Jack-in-office: a low-ranking, petty official
draught: draft; current of air
poker: an iron instrument used to stoke a fire

he spoke he picked up the steel poker and, with a sudden effort, straightened it out again.

"Fancy his having the insolence to confound me with the official detective force! This incident gives zest to our investigation, however, and I only trust that our little friend will not suffer from her imprudence in allowing this brute to trace her. And now, Watson, we shall order breakfast and afterwards I shall walk down to Doctors' Commons, where I hope to get some data which may help us in this matter."

It was nearly one o'clock when Sherlock Holmes returned from his excursion. He held in his hand a sheet of blue paper, scrawled over with notes and figures.

"I have seen the will of the deceased wife," said he. "To determine its exact meaning I have been obliged to work out the present prices of the investments with which it is concerned. The total income, which at the time of the wife's death was little short of £1100, is now, through the fall in agricultural prices, not more than £750. Each daughter can claim an income of £250, in case of marriage. It is evident, therefore, that if both girls had married, this beauty would have had a mere pittance, while even one of them would cripple him to a very serious extent. My morning's work has not been wasted, since it has proved that he has the very strongest motives for standing in the way of anything of the sort. And now, Watson, this is too serious for dawdling, especially as the old man is aware that we are interesting ourselves in his affairs; so if you are ready, we shall call a cab and drive to Waterloo. I should be very much obliged if you would slip your revolver in your pocket. An Eley's No. 2 is an excellent argument with gentlemen who can twist

---

fancy: imagine
insolence: rudeness
confound: confuse
zest: excitement
imprudence: carelessness
Doctors' Commons: the offices of a society of lawyers in London where public
    records were kept
pittance: a very small amount
dawdling: delaying
Eley's No. 2: a gun cartridge made by Eley Brothers in London

steel pokers into knots. That and a tooth-brush are, I think, all that we need."

At Waterloo we were fortunate in catching a train for Leatherhead, where we hired a trap at the station inn and drove for four or five miles through the lovely Surrey lanes. It was a perfect day, with a bright sun and a few fleecy clouds in the heavens. The trees and wayside hedges were just throwing out their first green shoots, and the air was full of the pleasant smell of the moist earth. To me at least there was a strange contrast between the sweet promise of the spring and this sinister quest upon which we were engaged. My companion sat in the front of the trap, his arms folded, his hat pulled down over his eyes, and his chin sunk upon his breast, buried in the deepest thought. Suddenly, however, he started, tapped me on the shoulder, and pointed over the meadows.

"Look there," said he.

A heavily timbered park stretched up in a gentle slope, thickening into a grove at the highest point. From amid the branches there jutted out the gray gables and high rooftree of a very old mansion.

"Stoke Moran?" said he.

"Yes, sir, that be the house of Dr. Grimesby Roylott," remarked the driver.

"There is some building going on there," said Holmes; "that is where we are going."

"There's the village," said the driver, pointing to a cluster of roofs some distance to the left; "but if you want to get to the house, you'll find it shorter to get over this stile, and so by the foot-path over the fields. There it is, where the lady is walking. "

"And the lady, I fancy, is Miss Stoner," observed Holmes, shading his eyes. "Yes, I think we had better do as you suggest."

We got off, paid our fare, and the trap rattled back on its way to Leatherhead.

"I thought it as well," said Holmes as we climbed the stile, "that this fellow should think we had come here as architects, or on some

---

trap: a horse-drawn carriage
gables: triangular roofs
stile: a small wooden structure, often with steps

definite business. It may stop his gossip. Good-afternoon, Miss Stoner. You see that we have been as good as our word."

Our client of the morning had hurried forward to meet us with a face which spoke her joy. "I have been waiting so eagerly for you," she cried, shaking hands with us warmly. "All has turned out splendidly. Dr. Roylott has gone to town; and it is unlikely that he will be back before evening."

"We have had the pleasure of making the doctor's acquaintance," said Holmes, and in a few words he sketched out what had occurred. Miss Stoner turned white to the lips as she listened.

"Good heavens!" she cried, "he has followed me, then."

"So it appears."

"He is so cunning that I never know when I am safe from him. What will he say when he returns?"

"He must guard himself, for he may find that there is someone more cunning than himself upon his track. You must lock yourself up from him to-night. If he is violent, we shall take you away to your aunt's at Harrow. Now, we must make the best use of our time, so kindly take us at once to the rooms which we are to examine."

The building was of gray, lichen-blotched stone, with a high central portion and two curving wings, like the claws of a crab, thrown out on each side. In one of these wings the windows were broken and blocked with wooden boards, while the roof was partly caved in, a picture of ruin. The central portion was in little better repair, but the right-hand block was comparatively modern, and the blinds in the windows, with the blue smoke curling up from the chimneys, showed that this was where the family resided. Some scaffolding had been erected against the end wall, and the stone-work had been broken into, but there were no signs of any workmen at the moment of our visit. Holmes walked slowly up and down the illtrimmed lawn and examined with deep attention the outsides of the windows.

"This, I take it, belongs to the room in which you used to sleep, the centre one to your sister's, and the one next to the main building to Dr. Roylott's chamber?"

"Exactly so. But I am now sleeping in the middle one."

"Pending the alterations, as I understand. By the way, there does not seem to be any pressing need for repairs at that end wall."

"There were none. I believe that it was an excuse to move me from my room."

"Ah! that is suggestive. Now, on the other side of this narrow wing runs the corridor from which these three rooms open. There are windows in it, of course?"

"Yes, but very small ones. Too narrow for anyone to pass through."

"As you both locked your doors at night, your rooms were unapproachable from that side. Now, would you have the kindness to go into your room and bar your shutters?"

Miss Stoner did so, and Holmes, after a careful examination through the open window, endeavoured in every way to force the shutter open, but without success. There was no slit through which a knife could be passed to raise the bar. Then with his lens he tested the hinges, but they were of solid iron, built firmly into the massive masonry. "Hum!" said he, scratching his chin in some perplexity, "my theory certainly presents some difficulties. No one could pass these shutters if they were bolted. Well, we shall see if the inside throws any light upon the matter."

A small side door led into the whitewashed corridor from which the three bedrooms opened. Holmes refused to examine the third chamber, so we passed at once to the second, that in which Miss Stoner was now sleeping, and in which her sister had met with her fate. It was a homely little room, with a low ceiling and a gaping fireplace, after the fashion of old country-houses. A brown chest of drawers stood in one corner, a narrow white-counterpaned bed in another, and a dressing-table on the left-hand side of the window. These articles, with two small wickerwork chairs, made up all the furniture in the room save for a square of Wilton carpet in the centre. The boards round and the panelling of the walls were of brown, worm-eaten oak, so old and discoloured that it may have dated from the original building of the house. Holmes drew one

---

pending: awaiting the conclusion of
lens: magnifying glass
masonry: brickwork

of the chairs into a corner and sat silent, while his eyes travelled round and round and up and down, taking in every detail of the apartment.

"Where does that bell communicate with?" he asked at last, pointing to a thick bell-rope which hung down beside the bed, the tassel actually lying upon the pillow.

"It goes to the housekeeper's room."

"It looks newer than the other things?"

"Yes, it was only put there a couple of years ago."

"Your sister asked for it, I suppose?"

"No, I never heard of her using it. We used always to get what we wanted for ourselves."

"Indeed, it seemed unnecessary to put so nice a bell there. You will excuse me for a few minutes while I satisfy myself as to this floor." He threw himself down upon his face with his lens in his hand and crawled swiftly backward and forward, examining minutely the cracks between the boards. Then he did the same with the woodwork with which the chamber was panelled. Finally he walked over to the bed and spent some time in staring at it and running his eye up and down the wall. Finally he took the bell-rope in his hand and gave it a brisk tug.

"Why, it's a dummy," said he.

"Won't it ring?"

"No, it is not even attached to a wire. This is very interesting. You can see now that it is fastened to a hook just above where the little opening for the ventilator is."

"How very absurd! I never noticed that before."

"Very strange!" muttered Holmes, pulling at the rope. "There are one or two very singular points about this room. For example, what a fool a builder must be to open a ventilator into another room, when, with the same trouble, he might have communicated with the outside air!"

"That is also quite modern," said the lady.

"Done about the same time as the bell-rope?" remarked Holmes.

"Yes, there were several little changes carried out about that time."

---

tassel: the fringed knot at the end of a rope or cord

"They seem to have been of a most interesting character—dummy bell-ropes, and ventilators which do not ventilate. With your permission, Miss Stoner, we shall now carry our researches into the inner apartment."

Dr. Grimesby Roylott's chamber was larger than that of his stepdaughter, but was as plainly furnished. A campbed, a small wooden shelf full of books, mostly of a technical character, an armchair beside the bed, a plain wooden chair against the wall, a round table, and a large iron safe were the principal things which met the eye. Holmes walked slowly round and examined each and all of them with the keenest interest.

"What's in here?" he asked, tapping the safe.

"My stepfather's business papers."

"Oh! you have seen inside, then?"

"Only once, some years ago. I remember that it was full of papers."

"There isn't a cat in it, for example?"

"No. What a strange idea!"

"Well, look at this!" He took up a small saucer of milk which stood on the top of it.

"No; we don't keep a cat. But there is a cheetah and a baboon."

"Ah, yes, of course! Well, a cheetah is just a big cat, and yet a saucer of milk does not go very far in satisfying its wants, I daresay. There is one point which I should wish to determine." He squatted down in front of the wooden chair and examined the seat of it with the greatest attention.

"Thank you. That is quite settled," said he, rising and putting his lens in his pocket. "Hello! Here is something interesting!"

The object which had caught his eyes was a small dog lash hung on one corner of the bed. The lash, however, was curled upon itself and tied so as to make a loop of whipcord.

"What do you make of that, Watson?"

"It's a common enough lash. But I don't know why it should be tied."

---

campbed: cot
whipcord: a strong cotton fabric twisted into a cord

"That is not quite so common, is it? Ah, me! it's a wicked world, and when a clever man turns his brains to crime it is the worst of all. I think that I have seen enough now, Miss Stoner, and with your permission we shall walk out upon the lawn."

I had never seen my friend's face so grim or his brow so dark as it was when we turned from the scene of this investigation. We had walked several times up and down the lawn, neither Miss Stoner nor myself liking to break in upon his thoughts before he roused himself from his reverie.

"It is very essential, Miss Stoner," said he, "that you should absolutely follow my advice in every respect."

"I shall most certainly do so."

"The matter is too serious for any hesitation. Your life may depend upon your compliance."

"I assure you that I am in your hands."

"In the first place, both my friend and I must spend the night in your room."

Both Miss Stoner and I gazed at him in astonishment.

"Yes, it must be so. Let me explain. I believe that that is the village inn over there?"

"Yes, that is the Crown."

"Very good. Your windows would be visible from there?"

"Certainly."

"You must confine yourself to your room, on pretence of a headache, when your stepfather comes back. Then when you hear him retire for the night, you must open the shutters of your window, undo the hasp, put your lamp there as a signal to us, and then withdraw quietly with everything which you are likely to want into the room which you used to occupy. I have no doubt that, in spite of the repairs, you could manage there for one night."

"Oh, yes, easily."

"The rest you will leave in our hands."

"But what will you do?"

---

reverie: trance
pretence: excuse
hasp: clasp

"We shall spend the night in your room, and we shall investigate the cause of this noise which has disturbed you."

"I believe, Mr. Holmes, that you have already made up your mind," said Miss Stoner, laying her hand upon my companion's sleeve.

"Perhaps I have."

"Then, for pity's sake, tell me what was the cause of my sister's death."

"I should prefer to have clearer proofs before I speak."

"You can at least tell me whether my own thought is correct, and if she died from some sudden fright."

"No, I do not think so. I think that there was probably some more tangible cause. And now, Miss Stoner, we must leave you, for if Dr. Roylott returned and saw us our journey would be in vain. Good-bye, and be brave, for if you will do what I have told you you may rest assured that we shall soon drive away the dangers which threaten you."

Sherlock Holmes and I had no difficulty in engaging a bedroom and sitting-room at the Crown Inn. They were on the upper floor, and from our window we could command a view of the avenue gate, and of the inhabited wing of Stoke Moran Manor House. At dusk we saw Dr. Grimesby Roylott drive past, his huge form looming up beside the little figure of the lad who drove him. The boy had some slight difficulty in undoing the heavy iron gates, and we heard the hoarse roar of the doctor's voice and saw the fury with which he shook his clinched fists at him. The trap drove on, and a few minutes later we saw a sudden light spring up among the trees as the lamp was lit in one of the sitting-rooms.

"Do you know, Watson," said Holmes as we sat together in the gathering darkness, "I have really some scruples as to taking you to-night. There is a distinct element of danger."

"Can I be of assistance?"

"Your presence might be invaluable."

"Then I shall certainly come."

"It is very kind of you."

---

tangible: concrete; physical
scruples: pangs of conscience; principles; worries

"You speak of danger. You have evidently seen more in these rooms than was visible to me."

"No, but I fancy that I may have deduced a little more. I imagine that you saw all that I did."

"I saw nothing remarkable save the bell-rope, and what purpose that could answer I confess is more than I can imagine."

"You saw the ventilator, too?"

"Yes, but I do not think that it is such a very unusual thing to have a small opening between two rooms. It was so small that a rat could hardly pass through."

"I knew that we should find a ventilator before ever we came to Stoke Moran."

"My dear Holmes!"

"Oh, yes, I did. You remember in her statement she said that her sister could smell Dr. Roylott s cigar. Now, of course that suggested at once that there must be a communication between the two rooms. It could only be a small one, or it would have been remarked upon at the coroner s inquiry. I deduced a ventilator."

"But what harm can there be in that?"

"Well, there is at least a curious coincidence of dates. A ventilator is made, a cord is hung, and a lady who sleeps in bed dies. Does not that strike you?"

"I cannot as yet see any connection."

"Did you observe anything very peculiar about that bed?"

"No."

"It was clamped to the floor. Did you ever see a bed fastened like that before?"

"I cannot say that I have."

"The lady could not move her bed. It must always be in the same relative position to the ventilator and to the rope—or so we may call it, since it was clearly never meant for a bell-pull."

"Holmes," I cried, "I seem to see dimly what you are hinting at. We are only just in time to prevent some subtle and horrible crime."

"Subtle and horrible enough. When a doctor does go wrong he is the first of criminals. He has nerve and he has knowledge. Palmer

first: best

94

and Pritchard were among the heads of their profession. This man strikes even deeper, but I think, Watson, that we shall be able to strike deeper still. But we shall have horrors enough before the night is over; for goodness' sake let us have a quiet pipe and turn our minds for a few hours to something more cheerful."

About nine o'clock the light among the trees was extinguished, and all was dark in the direction of the Manor House. Two hours passed slowly away, and then, suddenly, just at the stroke of eleven, a single bright light shone out right in front of us.

"That is our signal," said Holmes, springing to his feet; "it comes from the middle window."

As we passed out he exchanged a few words with the landlord, explaining that we were going on a late visit to an acquaintance, and that it was possible that we might spend the night there. A moment later we were out on the dark road, a chill wind blowing in our faces, and one yellow light twinkling in front of us through the gloom to guide us on our sombre errand.

There was little difficulty in entering the grounds, for unrepaired breaches gaped in the old park wall. Making our way among the trees, we reached the lawn, crossed it, and were about to enter through the window when out from a clump of laurel bushes there darted what seemed to be a hideous and distorted child, who threw itself upon the grass with writhing limbs and then ran swiftly across the lawn into the darkness.

"My God!" I whispered; "did you see it?"

Holmes was for the moment as startled as I. His hand closed like a vise upon my wrist in his agitation. Then he broke into a low laugh and put his lips to my ear.

"It is a nice household," he murmured. "That is the baboon."

I had forgotten the strange pets which the doctor affected. There was a cheetah, too; perhaps we might find it upon our shoulders at any moment. I confess that I felt easier in my mind when, after

---

Palmer and Pritchard: William Palmer and Edward Pritchard, two nineteenth-century English doctors convicted of poisoning members of their families
sombre: somber; serious
breaches: openings
agitation: nervous excitement

following Holmes's example and slipping off my shoes, I found myself inside the bedroom. My companion noiselessly closed the shutters, moved the lamp onto the table, and cast his eyes round the room. All was as we had seen it in the daytime. Then creeping up to me and making a trumpet of his hand, he whispered into my ear again so gently that it was all that I could do to distinguish the words:

"The least sound would be fatal to our plans."

I nodded to show that I had heard.

"We must sit without light. He would see it through the ventilator."

I nodded again.

"Do not go asleep; your very life may depend upon it. Have your pistol ready in case we should need it. I will sit on the side of the bed, and you in that chair."

I took out my revolver and laid it on the corner of the table.

Holmes had brought up a long thin cane, and this he placed upon the bed beside him. By it he laid the box of matches and the stump of a candle. Then he turned down the lamp, and we were left in darkness.

How shall I ever forget that dreadful vigil? I could not hear a sound, not even the drawing of a breath, and yet I knew that my companion sat open-eyed, within a few feet of me, in the same state of nervous tension in which I was myself. The shutters cut off the least ray of light, and we waited in absolute darkness. From outside came the occasional cry of a night-bird, and once at our very window a long drawn catlike whine, which told us that the cheetah was indeed at liberty. Far away we could hear the deep tones of the parish clock, which boomed out every quarter of an hour. How long they seemed, those quarters! Twelve struck, and one and two and three, and still we sat waiting silently for whatever might befall.

Suddenly there was the momentary gleam of a light up in the direction of the ventilator, which vanished immediately, but was succeeded by a strong smell of burning oil and heated metal.

---

vigil: sleepless watch

Someone in the next room had lit a dark-lantern. I heard a gentle sound of movement, and then all was silent once more, though the smell grew stronger. For half an hour I sat with straining ears. Then suddenly another sound became audible—a very gentle, soothing sound, like that of a small jet of steam escaping continually from a kettle. The instant that we heard it, Holmes sprang from the bed, struck a match, and lashed furiously with his cane at the bell-pull. "You see it, Watson?" he yelled. "You see it?"

But I saw nothing. At the moment when Holmes struck the light, I heard a low, clear whistle, but the sudden glare flashing into my weary eyes made it impossible for me to tell what it was at which my friend lashed so savagely. I could, however, see that his face was deadly pale and filled with horror and loathing.

He had ceased to strike and was gazing up at the ventilator when suddenly there broke from the silence of the night the most horrible cry to which I have ever listened. It swelled up louder and louder, a hoarse yell of pain and fear and anger all mingled in the one dreadful shriek. They say that away down in the village, and even in the distant parsonage, that cry raised the sleepers from their beds. It struck cold to our hearts, and I stood gazing at Holmes, and he at me, until the last, echoes of it died away into the silence from which it rose.

"What can it mean?" I gasped.

"It means that it is all over," Holmes answered. "And perhaps, after all, it is for the best. Take your pistol, and we will enter Dr. Roylott's room."

With a grave face he lit the lamp and led the way down the corridor. Twice he struck at the chamber door without any reply from within. Then he turned the handle and entered, I at his heels, with the cocked pistol in my hand.

It was a singular sight which met our eyes. On the table stood a dark-lantern with the shutter half open, throwing a brilliant beam of light upon the iron safe, the door of which was ajar. Beside this table, on the wooden chair, sat Dr. Grimesby Roylott, clad in a

---

dark-lantern: a lantern with a sliding panel to hide its light
lashed: struck
loathing: hatred
parsonage: church house; rectory

long gray dressing-gown, his bare ankles protruding beneath, and his feet thrust into red heelless Turkish slippers. Across his lap lay the short stock with the long lash which we had noticed during the day. His chin was cocked upward and his eyes were fixed in a dreadful, rigid stare at the corner of the ceiling. Round his brow he had a peculiar yellow band, with brownish speckles, which seemed to be bound tightly round his head. As we entered he made neither sound nor motion.

"The band! the speckled band!" whispered Holmes.

I took a step forward. In an instant his strange headgear began to move, and there reared itself from among his hair the squat diamond-shaped head and puffed neck of a loathsome serpent.

"It is a swamp adder!" cried Holmes; "the deadliest snake in India. He has died within ten seconds of being bitten. Violence does, in truth, recoil upon the violent, and the schemer falls into the pit which he digs for another. Let us thrust this creature back into its den, and we can then remove Miss Stoner to some place of shelter and let the county police know what has happened."

As he spoke he drew the dog-whip swiftly from the dead man's lap, and throwing the noose round the reptile's neck he drew it from its horrid perch and, carrying it at arm's length, threw it into the iron safe, which he closed upon it.

Such are the true facts of the death of Dr. Grimesby Roylott, of Stoke Moran. It is not necessary that I should prolong a narrative which has already run to too great a length by telling how we broke the sad news to the terrified girl, how we conveyed her by the morning train to the care of her good aunt at Harrow, of how the slow process of official inquiry came to the conclusion that the doctor met his fate while indiscreetly playing with a dangerous pet. The little which I had yet to learn of the case was told me by Sherlock Holmes as we travelled back next day.

"I had," said he, "come to an entirely erroneous conclusion which shows, my dear Watson, how dangerous it always is to reason from insufficient data. The presence of the gypsies, and

---

protruding: sticking out
indiscreetly: carelessly

the use of the word 'band,' which was used by the poor girl, no doubt to explain the appearance which she had caught a hurried glimpse of by the light of her match, were sufficient to put me upon an entirely wrong scent. I can only claim the merit that I instantly reconsidered my position when, however, it became clear to me that whatever danger threatened an occupant of the room could not come either from the window or the door. My attention was speedily drawn, as I have already remarked to you, to this ventilator, and to the bell-rope which hung down to the bed. The discovery that this was a dummy, and that the bed was clamped to the floor, instantly gave rise to the suspicion that the rope was there as a bridge for something passing through the hole and coming to the bed. The idea of a snake instantly occurred to me, and when I coupled it with my knowledge that the doctor was furnished with a supply of creatures from India, I felt that I was probably on the right track. The idea of using a form of poison which could not possibly be discovered by any chemical test was just such a one as would occur to a clever and ruthless man who had had an Eastern training. The rapidity with which such a poison would take effect would also, from his point of view, be an advantage. It would be a sharp-eyed coroner, indeed, who could distinguish the two little dark punctures which would show where the poison fangs had done their work. Then I thought of the whistle. Of course he must recall the snake before the morning light revealed it to the victim. He had trained it, probably by the use of the milk which we saw, to return to him when summoned. He would put it through this ventilator at the hour that he thought best, with the certainty that it would crawl down the rope and land on the bed. It might or might not bite the occupant, perhaps she might escape every night for a week, but sooner or later she must fall a victim.

"I had come to these conclusions before ever I had entered his room. An inspection of his chair showed me that he had been in the habit of standing on it, which of course would be necessary in order that he should reach the ventilator. The sight of the safe, the saucer of milk, and the loop of whipcord were enough to finally dispel any doubts which may have remained. The metallic clang heard by Miss Stoner was obviously caused by her stepfather hastily closing the door of his safe upon its terrible occupant. Having once made up my mind, you know the steps which I took in order to put the matter to the proof. I heard the creature hiss as I have no doubt that you did also, and I instantly lit the light and attacked it."

"With the result of driving it through the ventilator."

"And also with the result of causing it to turn upon its master at the other side. Some of the blows of my cane came home and roused its snakish temper, so that it flew upon the first person it saw. In this way I am no doubt indirectly responsible for Dr. Grimesby Roylott's death, and I cannot say that it is likely to weigh very heavily upon my conscience."

roused: awoke

THE BOSCOMBE VALLEY MYSTERY

Sir Arthur Conan Doyle

In this tale from 1891, Sherlock Holmes's faithful companion, Dr. John H. Watson, describes an apparently open-and-shut murder case that Holmes is called to investigate in the west of England. Holmes uses his powers of observation and deduction to demonstrate, as he puts it, that "there is nothing more deceptive than an obvious fact."

We were seated at breakfast one morning, my wife and I, when the maid brought in a telegram. It was from Sherlock Holmes and ran in this way:

> Have you a couple of days to spare? Have just been wired for from the west of England in connection with Boscombe Valley tragedy. Shall be glad if you will come with me. Air and scenery perfect. Leave Paddington by the 11:15.

"What do you say, dear?" said my wife, looking across at me. "Will you go?"

"I really don't know what to say. I have a fairly long list at present."

"Oh, Anstruther would do your work for you. You have been looking a little pale lately. I think that the change would do you good, and you are always so interested in Sherlock Holmes's cases."

"I should be ungrateful if I were not, seeing what I gained through one of them," I answered. "But if I am to go, I must pack at once, for I have only half an hour."

been wired for: received a telegram
Paddington: Paddington Station, one of the major train stations in London
Anstruther: a fictional character, a fellow doctor who took over Watson's medical
    cases when Watson went away to assist Holmes

My experience of camp life in Afghanistan had at least had the effect of making me a prompt and ready traveller. My wants were few and simple, so that in less than the time stated I was in a cab with my valise, rattling away to Paddington Station. Sherlock Holmes was pacing up and down the platform, his tall, gaunt figure made even gaunter and taller by his long gray travelling-cloak and close-fitting cloth cap.

"It is really very good of you to come, Watson," said he. "It makes a considerable difference to me, having someone with me on whom I can thoroughly rely. Local aid is always either worthless or else biassed. If you will keep the two corner seats I shall get the tickets."

We had the carriage to ourselves save for an immense litter of papers which Holmes had brought with him. Among these he rummaged and read, with intervals of note-taking and of meditation, until we were past Reading. Then he suddenly rolled them all into a gigantic ball and tossed them up onto the rack.

"Have you heard anything of the case?" he asked.

"Not a word. I have not seen a paper for some days."

"The London press has not had very full accounts. I have just been looking through all the recent papers in order to master the particulars. It seems, from what I gather, to be one of those simple cases which are so extremely difficult."

"That sounds a little paradoxical."

"But it is profoundly true. Singularity is almost invariably a clue. The more featureless and commonplace a crime is, the more difficult it is to bring it home. In this case, however, they have established a very serious case against the son of the murdered man."

"It is a murder, then?"

---

valise: suitcase
gaunt: lean; thin
meditation: deep thought
Reading: a large town west of London
paradoxical: self-contradictory
singularity: uniqueness; unusualness
invariably: always; in all cases

"Well, it is conjectured to be so. I shall take nothing for granted until I have the opportunity of looking personally into it. I will explain the state of things to you, as far as I have been able to understand it, in a very few words.

"Boscombe Valley is a country district not very far from Ross, in Herefordshire. The largest landed proprietor in that part is a Mr. John Turner, who made his money in Australia and returned some years ago to the old country. One of the farms which he held, that of Hatherley, was let to Mr. Charles McCarthy, who was also an ex-Australian. The men had known each other in the colonies, so that it was not unnatural that when they came to settle down they should do so as near each other as possible. Turner was apparently the richer man, so McCarthy became his tenant but still remained, it seems, upon terms of perfect equality, as they were frequently together. McCarthy had one son, a lad of eighteen, and Turner had an only daughter of the same age, but neither of them had wives living. They appear to have avoided the society of the neighbouring English families and to have led retired lives, though both the McCarthys were fond of sport and were frequently seen at the race-meeting of the neighbourhood. McCarthy kept two servants—a man and a girl. Turner had a considerable household, some half-dozen at the least. That is as much as I have been able to gather about the families. Now for the facts.

"On June 3d, that is, on Monday last, McCarthy left his house at Hatherley about three in the afternoon and walked down to the Boscombe Pool, which is a small lake formed by the spreading out of the stream which runs down the Boscombe Valley. He had been out with his serving-man in the morning at Ross, and he had told the man that he must hurry, as he had an appointment of importance to keep at three. From that appointment he never came back alive.

"From Hatherley Farmhouse to the Boscombe Pool is a quarter of a mile, and two people saw him as he passed over this ground. One was an old woman, whose name is not mentioned, and the

conjectured: thought; believed
Herefordshire: a county in the west of England that borders Wales
let: rented

other was William Crowder, a gamekeeper in the employ of
Mr. Turner. Both these witnesses depose that Mr. McCarthy was
walking alone. The gamekeeper adds that within a few minutes
of his seeing Mr. McCarthy pass he had seen his son, Mr. James
McCarthy, going the same way with a gun under his arm. To the
best of his belief, the father was actually in sight at the time, and
the son was following him. He thought no more of the matter until
he heard in the evening of the tragedy that had occurred.

"The two McCarthys were seen after the time when William
Crowder, the game-keeper, lost sight of them. The Boscombe Pool
is thickly wooded round, with just a fringe of grass and of reeds
round the edge. A girl of fourteen, Patience Moran, who is the
daughter of the lodge-keeper of the Boscombe Valley estate, was
in one of the woods picking flowers. She states that while she was
there she saw, at the border of the wood and close by the lake,
Mr. McCarthy and his son, and that they appeared to be having
a violent quarrel. She heard Mr. McCarthy the elder using very
strong language to his son, and she saw the latter raise up his hand
as if to strike his father. She was so frightened by their violence
that she ran away and told her mother when she reached home
that she had left the two McCarthys quarrelling near Boscombe
Pool, and that she was afraid that they were going to fight. She
had hardly said the words when young McCarthy came running
up to the lodge to say he had found his father dead in the wood,
and to ask for the help of the lodge-keeper. He was much excited,
without either his gun or his hat, and his right hand and sleeve
were observed to be stained with fresh blood. On following him
they found the dead body stretched out upon the grass beside
the pool. The head had been beaten in by repeated blows of some
heavy and blunt weapon. The injuries were such as might very well
have been inflicted by the butt-end of his son's gun, which was
found lying on the grass within a few paces of the body. Under
these circumstances the young man was instantly arrested, and a
verdict of 'wilful murder' having been returned at the inquest on

---

depose: swear or declare under oath
inquest: an official inquiry into an unexpected and possibly unlawful death

Tuesday, he was on Wednesday brought before the magistrates at Ross, who have referred the case to the next Assizes. Those are the main facts of the case as they came out before the coroner and the police-court."

"I could hardly imagine a more damning case," I remarked. "If ever circumstantial evidence pointed to a criminal it does so here."

"Circumstantial evidence is a very tricky thing," answered Holmes thoughtfully. "It may seem to point very straight to one thing, but if you shift your own point of view a little, you may find it pointing in an equally uncompromising manner to something entirely different. It must be confessed, however, that the case looks exceedingly grave against the young man, and it is very possible that he is indeed the culprit. There are several people in the neighbourhood, however, and among them Miss Turner, the daughter of the neighbouring landowner, who believe in his innocence, and who have retained Lestrade, whom you may recollect in connection with 'A Study in Scarlet,' to work out the case in his interest. Lestrade, being rather puzzled, has referred the case to me, and hence it is that two middle-aged gentlemen are flying westward at fifty miles an hour instead of quietly digesting their breakfasts at home."

"I am afraid" said I, "that the facts are so obvious that you will find little credit to be gained out of this case."

"There is nothing more deceptive than an obvious fact," he answered, laughing. "Besides, we may chance to hit upon some other obvious facts which may have been by no means obvious to Mr. Lestrade. You know me too well to think that I am boasting when I say that I shall either confirm or destroy his theory by means which he is quite incapable of employing, or even of understanding. To take the first example to hand, I very clearly perceive that in your bedroom the window is upon the right-hand side, and

---

magistrates: judges
the next Assizes: the next session of the county courts
coroner: one who conducts autopsies to determine causes of death
uncompromising: direct
grave: serious
culprit: guilty party
retained: hired
"A Study in Scarlet": title of an earlier case solved by Holmes

yet I question whether Mr. Lestrade would have noted even so self-evident a thing as that."

"How on earth—"

"My dear fellow, I know you well. I know the military neatness which characterizes you. You shave every morning, and in this season you shave by the sunlight; but since your shaving is less and less complete as we get farther back on the left side, until it becomes positively slovenly as we get round the angle of the jaw, it is surely very clear that that side is less illuminated than the other. I could not imagine a man of your habits looking at himself in an equal light and being satisfied with such a result. I only quote this as a trivial example of observation and inference. Therein lies my *métier*, and it is just possible that it may be of some service in the investigation which lies before us. There are one or two minor points which were brought out in the inquest, and which are worth considering."

"What are they?"

"It appears that his arrest did not take place at once, but after the return to Hatherley Farm. On the inspector of constabulary informing him that he was a prisoner, he remarked that he was not surprised to hear it, and that it was no more than his deserts. This observation of his had the natural effect of removing any traces of doubt which might have remained in the minds of the coroner's jury."

"It was a confession," I ejaculated.

"No, for it was followed by a protestation of innocence."

"Coming on the top of such a damning series of events, it was at least a most suspicious remark."

"On the contrary," said Holmes, "it is the brightest rift which I can at present see in the clouds. However innocent he might be, he could not be such an absolute imbecile as not to see that

---

slovenly: messy; careless
inference: a deduction or an educated guess
métier: vocation; special expertise
constabulary: police department
his deserts: what he deserves
ejaculated: exclaimed
rift: crack; opening

the circumstances were very black against him. Had he appeared surprised at his own arrest, or feigned indignation at it, I should have looked upon it as highly suspicious, because such surprise or anger would not be natural under the circumstances, and yet might appear to be the best policy to a scheming man. His frank acceptance of the situation marks him as either an innocent man, or else as a man of considerable self-restraint and firmness. As to his remark about his deserts, it was also not unnatural if you consider that he stood beside the dead body of his father, and that there is no doubt that he had that very day so far forgotten his filial duty as to bandy words with him, and even, according to the little girl whose evidence is so important, to raise his hand as if to strike him. The self-reproach and contrition which are displayed in his remark appear to me to be the signs of a healthy mind rather than of a guilty one."

I shook my head. "Many men have been hanged on far slighter evidence," I remarked.

"So they have. And many men have been wrongfully hanged."

"What is the young man's own account of the matter?"

"It is, I am afraid, not very encouraging to his supporters, though there are one or two points in it which are suggestive. You will find it here, and may read it for yourself."

He picked out from his bundle a copy of the local Herefordshire paper, and having turned down the sheet he pointed out the paragraph in which the unfortunate young man had given his own statement of what had occurred. I settled myself down in the corner of the carriage and read it very carefully. It ran in this way:

> Mr. James McCarthy, the only son of the deceased, was then called and gave evidence as follows: "I had been away from home for three days at Bristol, and had only just returned upon the morning of last Monday, the 3d. My father was absent from home at the time of my arrival,

feigned: faked; pretended
filial duty: responsibilities associated with or related to being a son or daughter
bandy: exchange words (usually in argument)
self-reproach: self-criticism
contrition: sorrow; regret

and I was informed by the maid that he had driven over to Ross with John Cobb, the groom. Shortly after my return I heard the wheels of his trap in the yard, and, looking out of my window, I saw him get out and walk rapidly out of the yard, though I was not aware in which direction he was going. I then took my gun and strolled out in the direction of the Boscombe Pool, with the intention of visiting the rabbit-warren which is upon the other side. On my way I saw William Crowder, the game-keeper, as he had stated in his evidence; but he is mistaken in thinking that I was following my father. I had no idea that he was in front of me. When about a hundred yards from the pool I heard a cry of 'Cooee!' which was a usual signal between my father and myself. I then hurried forward, and found him standing by the pool. He appeared to be much surprised at seeing me and asked me rather roughly what I was doing there. A conversation ensued which led to high words and almost to blows, for my father was a man of a very violent temper. Seeing that his passion was becoming ungovernable, I left him and returned towards Hatherley Farm. I had not gone more than 150 yards, however, when I heard a hideous outcry behind me, which caused me to run back again. I found my father expiring upon the ground, with his head terribly injured. I dropped my gun and held him in my arms, but he almost instantly expired. I knelt beside him for some minutes, and then made my way to Mr. Turner's lodge-keeper, his house being the nearest, to ask for assistance. I saw no one near my father when I returned, and I have no idea how he came by his injuries. He was not a popular man, being somewhat cold and forbidding in his manners; but he had, as far as I know, no active enemies. I know nothing further of the matter."

---

groom: one who cares for horses; a stableman
trap: a horse-drawn carriage
rabbit-warren: a series of tunnels where rabbits live
ensued: followed
expired: died

The Coroner: Did your father make any statement to you before he died?

Witness: He mumbled a few words, but I could only catch some allusion to a rat.

The Coroner: What did you understand by that?

Witness: It conveyed no meaning to me. I thought that he was delirious.

The Coroner: What was the point upon which you and your father had this final quarrel?

Witness: I should prefer not to answer.

The Coroner: I am afraid that I must press it.

Witness: It is really impossible for me to tell you. I can assure that it has nothing to do with the sad tragedy which followed.

The Coroner: That is for the court to decide. I need not point out to you that your refusal to answer will prejudice your case considerably in any future proceedings which may arise.

Witness: I must still refuse.

The Coroner: I understand that the cry of "Cooee" was a common signal between you and your father?

Witness: It was.

The Coroner: How was it, then, that he uttered it before he saw you, and before he even knew that you had returned from Bristol?

Witness: (with considerable confusion): I do not know.

A Juryman: Did you see nothing which aroused your suspicions when you returned on hearing the cry and found your father fatally injured?

Witness: Nothing definite.

The Coroner: What do you mean?

Witness: I was so disturbed and excited as I rushed out into the open, that I could think of nothing except of my father. Yet I have a vague impression that as I ran forward something lay upon the ground to the left of me. It seemed to me to be something gray in colour, a coat of some sort or a plaid perhaps. When I rose from my father I looked round for it, but it was gone."

---

delirious: in a state of mental confusion or disturbance

"Do you mean that it disappeared before you went for help?"

"Yes, it was gone."

"You cannot say what it was?"

"No, I had a feeling something was there."

"How far from the body?"

"A dozen yards or so."

"And how far from the edge of the wood?"

"About the same."

"Then if it was removed it was while you were within a dozen yards of it?"

"Yes, but with my back towards it."

This concluded the examination of the witness.

"I see," said I as I glanced down the column, "that the coroner in his concluding remarks was rather severe upon young McCarthy. He calls attention, and with reason, to the discrepancy about his father having signalled to him before seeing him, also to his refusal to give details of his conversation with his father, and his singular account of his father's dying words. They are all, as he remarks, very much against the son."

Holmes laughed softly to himself and stretched himself out upon the cushioned seat. "Both you and the coroner have been at some pains," said he, "to single out the very strongest points in the young man's favour. Don't you see that you alternately give him credit for having too much imagination and too little? Too little, if he could not invent a cause of quarrel which would give him the sympathy of the jury; too much, if he evolved from his own inner consciousness anything so *outré* as a dying reference to a rat, and the incident of the vanishing cloth. No, sir, I shall approach this case from the point of view that what this young man says is true, and we shall see whither that hypothesis will lead us. And now here is my pocket Petrarch, and not another word shall I say of this case until we are on the scene of action. We lunch at Swindon, and I see that we shall be there in twenty minutes."

---

discrepancy: inconsistency
outré: bizarre
Petrarch: fourteenth-century Italian scholar and poet, famous for his sonnets
Swindon: a large town about 40 miles east of Reading and 80 miles east of London

It was nearly four o'clock when we at last, after passing through the beautiful Stroud Valley, and over the broad gleaming Severn, found ourselves at the pretty little country-town of Ross. A lean, ferret-like man, furtive and sly-looking, was waiting for us upon the platform. In spite of the light brown dustcoat and leather-leggings which he wore in deference to his rustic surroundings. I had no difficulty in recognizing Lestrade, of Scotland Yard. With him we drove to the Hereford Arms where a room had already been engaged for us.

"I have ordered a carriage," said Lestrade as we sat over a cup of tea. "I knew your energetic nature, and that you would not be happy until you had been on the scene of the crime."

"It was very nice and complimentary of you," Holmes answered. "It is entirely a question of barometric pressure."

Lestrade looked startled. "I do not quite follow," he said.

"How is the glass? Twenty-nine, I see. No wind, and not a cloud in the sky. I have a caseful of cigarettes here which need smoking, and the sofa is very much superior to the usual country hotel abomination. I do not think that it is probable that I shall use the carriage to-night. "

Lestrade laughed indulgently. "You have, no doubt, already formed your conclusions from the newspapers," he said. "The case is as plain as a pikestaff, and the more one goes into it the plainer it becomes. Still, of course, one can't refuse a lady, and such a very positive one, too. She had heard of you, and would have your opinion, though I repeatedly told her that there was nothing which

---

Stroud Valley: a valley in southwestern England
Severn: the Severn River, the longest river in Great Britain
furtive: sneaky
leather-leggings: chaps
deference: regard
rustic: rural
Scotland Yard: the detective department of London's Metropolitan Police Service
engaged: reserved
barometric pressure: atmospheric pressure, as measured by a barometer
glass: barometer; a tool for measuring atmospheric pressure
abomination: disgrace
indulgently: tolerantly

you could do which I had not already done. Why, bless my soul! here is her carriage at the door."

He had hardly spoken before there rushed into the room one of the most lovely young women that I have ever seen in my life. Her violet eyes were shining, her lips parted, a pink flush upon her cheeks, all thought of her natural reserve lost in her overpowering excitement and concern.

"Oh, Mr. Sherlock Holmes!" she cried, glancing from one to the other of us, and finally, with a woman's quick intuition, fastening upon my companion, "I am so glad that you have come. I have driven down to tell you so. I know that James didn't do it. I know it, and I want you to start upon your work knowing it, too. Never let yourself doubt upon that point. We have known each other since we were little children, and I know his faults as no one else does; but he is too tenderhearted to hurt a fly. Such a charge is absurd to anyone who really knows him."

"I hope we may clear him, Miss Turner," said Sherlock Holmes. "You may rely upon my doing all that I can."

"But you have read the evidence. You have formed some conclusion? Do you not see some loophole, some flaw? Do you not yourself think that he is innocent?"

"I think that it is very probable."

"There, now!" she cried, throwing back her head and looking defiantly at Lestrade. "You hear! He gives me hopes."

Lestrade shrugged his shoulders. "I am afraid that my colleague has been a little quick in forming his conclusions," he said.

"But he is right. Oh! I know that he is right. James never did it. And about his quarrel with his father, I am sure that the reason why he would not speak about it to the coroner was because I was concerned in it."

"In what way?" asked Holmes.

"It is no time for me to hide anything. James and his father had many disagreements about me. Mr. McCarthy was very anxious that there should be a marriage between us. James and I have always loved each other as brother and sister; but of course he is young and has seen very little of life yet, and—and—well, he

---

reserve: restraint

112

naturally did not wish to do anything like that yet. So there were quarrels, and this, I am sure, was one of them."

"And your father?" asked Holmes. "Was he in favour of such a union?"

"No, he was averse to it also. No one but Mr. McCarthy was in favour of it." A quick blush passed over her fresh young face as Holmes shot one of his keen, questioning glances at her.

"Thank you for this information," said he. "May I see your father if I call tomorrow?"

"I am afraid the doctor won't allow it."

"The doctor?"

"Yes, have you not heard? Poor father has never been strong for years back, but this has broken him down completely. He has taken to his bed, and Dr. Willows says that he is a wreck and that his nervous system is shattered. Mr. McCarthy was the only man alive who had known dad in the old days in Victoria."

"Ha! In Victoria! That is important."

"Quite so; at the gold-mines, where, as I understand, Mr. Turner made his money."

"Yes, certainly."

"Thank you, Miss Turner. You have been of material assistance to me."

"You will tell me if you have any news tomorrow. No doubt you will go to the prison to see James. Oh, if you do, Mr. Holmes, do tell him that I know him to be innocent."

"I will, Miss Turner."

"I must go home now, for dad is very ill, and he misses me so if I leave him. Good-bye, and God help you in your undertaking." She hurried from the room as impulsively as she had entered, and we heard the wheels of her carriage rattle off down the street.

"I am ashamed of you, Holmes," said Lestrade with dignity after a few minutes' silence. "Why should you raise up hopes which you are bound to disappoint? I am not over-tender of heart, but I call it cruel."

---

averse: opposed
keen: intense
Victoria: an area in southeastern Australia where gold was discovered in 1851

"I think that I see my way to clearing James McCarthy," said Holmes. "Have you an order to see him in prison?"

"Yes, but only for you and me."

"Then I shall reconsider my resolution about going out. We have still time to take a train to Hereford and see him to-night?"

"Ample."

"Then let us do so. Watson, I fear that you will find it very slow, but I shall only be away a couple of hours."

I walked down to the station with them, and then wandered through the streets of the little town, finally returning to the hotel, where I lay upon the sofa and tried to interest myself in a yellow-backed novel. The puny plot of the story was so thin, however, when compared to the deep mystery through which we were groping, and I found my attention wander so continually from the fiction to the fact, that I at last flung it across the room and gave myself up entirely to a consideration of the events of the day. Supposing that this unhappy young man's story were absolutely true, then what hellish thing, what absolutely unforeseen and extraordinary calamity could have occurred between the time when he parted from his father, and the moment when, drawn back by his screams, he rushed into the glade? It was something terrible and deadly. What could it be? Might not the nature of the injuries reveal something to my medical instincts? I rang the bell and called for the weekly county paper, which contained a verbatim account of the inquest. In the surgeon's deposition it was stated that the posterior third of the left parietal bone and the left half of the occipital bone had been shattered by a heavy blow from a blunt weapon. I marked the spot upon my own head. Clearly such a blow must have been struck from behind. That was to some extent in favour of the accused, as when seen quarreling he was face to face with his father. Still, it did not go for very much, for

---

ample: plenty
calamity: tragedy
glade: an open space in a wooded area
verbatim: word for word; exact
posterior: rear
parietal bone: a bone in the side of the skull
occipital bone: a bone in the back of the head, above eye level

the older man might have turned his back before the blow fell. Still, it might be worth while to call Holmes's attention to it. Then there was the peculiar dying reference to a rat. What could that mean? It could not be delirium. A man dying from a sudden blow does not commonly become delirious. No, it was more likely to be an attempt to explain how he met his fate. But what could it indicate? I cudgelled my brains to find some possible explanation. And then the incident of the gray cloth seen by young McCarthy. If that were true the murderer must have dropped some part of his dress, presumably his overcoat, in his flight, and must have had the hardihood to return and to carry it away at the instant when the son was kneeling with his back turned not a dozen paces off. What a tissue of mysteries and improbabilities the whole thing was! I did not wonder at Lestrade's opinion, and yet I had so much faith in Sherlock Holmes's insight that I could not lose hope as long as every fresh fact seemed to strengthen his conviction of young McCarthy's innocence.

It was late before Sherlock Holmes returned. He came back alone, for Lestrade was staying in lodgings in the town.

"The glass still keeps very high," he remarked as he sat down. "It is of importance that it should not rain before we are able to go over the ground. On the other hand, a man should be at his very best and keenest for such nice work as that, and I did not wish to do it when fagged by a long journey. I have seen young McCarthy."

"And what did you learn from him?"

"Nothing."

"Could he throw no light?"

"None at all. I was inclined to think at one time that he knew who had done it and was screening him or her, but I am convinced now that he is as puzzled as everyone else. He is not a very quick-witted youth, though comely to look at and, I should think, sound at heart."

---

cudgelled: beat
hardihood: boldness; resoluteness
fagged: tired out
screening: protecting

"I cannot admire his taste," I remarked, "if it is indeed a fact that he was averse to a marriage with so charming a young lady as this Miss Turner."

"Ah, thereby hangs a rather painful tale. This fellow is madly, insanely, in love with her, but some two years ago, when he was only a lad, and before he really knew her, for she had been away five years at a boarding-school, what does the idiot do but get into the clutches of a barmaid in Bristol and marry her at a registry office? No one knows a word of the matter, but you can imagine how maddening it must be to him to be upbraided for not doing what he would give his very eyes to do, but what he knows to be absolutely impossible. It was sheer frenzy of this sort which made him throw his hands up into the air when his father, at their last interview, was goading him on to propose to Miss Turner. On the other hand, he had no means of supporting himself, and his father, who was by all accounts a very hard man, would have thrown him over utterly had he known the truth. It was with his barmaid wife that he had spent the last three days in Bristol, and his father did not know where he was. Mark that point. It is of importance. Good has come out of evil, however, for the barmaid, finding from the papers that he is in serious trouble and likely to be hanged, has thrown him over utterly and has written to him to say that she has a husband already in the Bermuda Dockyard, so that there is really no tie between them. I think that that bit of news has consoled young McCarthy for all that he has suffered."

"But if he is innocent, who has done it?"

"Ah! who? I would call your attention very particularly to two points. One is that the murdered man had an appointment with someone at the pool, and that the someone could not have been his son, for his son was away, and he did not know when he would return. The second is that the murdered man was heard to cry 'Cooee!' before he knew that his son had returned. Those are the crucial points upon which the case depends. And now let us talk

upbraided: criticized; scolded
goading: urging
Bermuda Dockyard: a dockyard of the Royal Navy that was opened on an island in
    Bermuda in 1809

116

about George Meredith, if you please, and we shall leave all minor matters until to-morrow."

There was no rain, as Holmes had foretold, and the morning broke bright and cloudless. At nine o'clock Lestrade called for us with the carriage, and we set off for Hatherley Farm and the Boscombe Pool.

"There is serious news this morning," Lestrade observed. "It is said that Mr. Turner, of the Hall, is so ill that his life is despaired of."

"An elderly man, I presume?" said Holmes.

"About sixty; but his constitution has been shattered by his life abroad, and he has been in failing health for some time. This business had had a very bad effect upon him. He was an old friend of McCarthy's, and, I may add, a great benefactor to him, for I have learned that he gave him Hatherley Farm rent free."

"Indeed! That is interesting," said Holmes.

"Oh, yes! In a hundred other ways he has helped him. Everybody about here speaks of his kindness to him."

"Really! Does it not strike you as a little singular that this McCarthy, who appears to have had little of his own, and to have been under such obligations to Turner, should still talk of marrying his son to Turner's daughter, who is, presumably, heiress to the estate, and that in such a very cocksure manner, as if it were merely a case of a proposal and all else would follow? It is the more strange, since we know that Turner himself was averse to the idea. The daughter told us as much. Do you not deduce something from that?"

"We have got to the deductions and the inferences," said Lestrade, winking at me. "I find it hard enough to tackle facts, Holmes, without flying away after theories and fancies."

"You are right," said Holmes demurely; "you do find it very hard to tackle the facts."

"Anyhow, I have grasped one fact which you seem to find it difficult to get hold of," replied Lestrade with some warmth.

"And that is—"

---

constitution: a person's physical makeup or state of health
benefactor: supporter
cocksure: excessively confident
fancies: wild ideas

117

"That McCarthy senior met his death from McCarthy junior and that all theories to the contrary are the merest moonshine."

"Well, moonshine is a brighter thing than fog," said Holmes, laughing. "But I am very much mistaken if this is not Hatherley Farm upon the left."

"Yes, that is it." It was a widespread, comfortable-looking building, two-storied, slate-roofed, with great yellow blotches of lichen upon the gray walls. The drawn blinds and the smokeless chimneys, however, gave it a stricken look, as though the weight of this horror still lay heavy upon it. We called at the door, when the maid, at Holmes's request, showed us the boots which her master wore at the time of his death, and also a pair of the son's, though not the pair which he had then had. Having measured these very carefully from seven or eight different points, Holmes desired to be led to the court-yard, from which we all followed the winding track which led to Boscombe Pool.

Sherlock Holmes was transformed when he was hot upon such a scent as this. Men who had only known the quiet thinker and logician of Baker Street would have failed to recognize him. His face flushed and darkened. His brows were drawn into two hard black lines, while his eyes shone out from beneath them with a steely glitter. His face was bent downward, his shoulders bowed, his lips compressed, and the veins stood out like whipcord in his long, sinewy neck. His nostrils seemed to dilate with a purely animal lust for the chase, and his mind was so absolutely concentrated upon the matter before him that a question or remark fell unheeded upon his ears, or, at the most, only provoked a quick, impatient snarl in reply. Swiftly and silently he made his way along the track which ran through the meadows, and so by way of the woods to the Boscombe Pool. It was damp, marshy ground, as is all that district, and there were marks of many feet, both upon the path and amid

the merest moonshine: as insubstantial and dim as moonlight
lichen: an organism made up of an algae and a fungus
stricken: ill or injured
Baker Street: Holmes's home in London is an apartment at 221B Baker Street
whipcord: a strong cotton fabric twisted into a cord
sinewy: full of tendons
dilate: expand

the short grass which bounded it on either side. Sometimes Holmes would hurry on, sometimes stop dead, and once he made quite a little detour into the meadow. Lestrade and I walked behind him, the detective indifferent and contemptuous, while I watched my friend with the interest which sprang from the conviction that every one of his actions was directed towards a definite end.

The Boscombe Pool, which is a little reed-girt sheet of water some fifty yards across, is situated at the boundary between the Hatherley Farm and the private park of the wealthy Mr. Turner. Above the woods which lined it upon the farther side we could see the red, jutting pinnacles which marked the site of the rich landowner's dwelling. On the Hatherley side of the pool the woods grew very thick, and there was a narrow belt of sodden grass twenty paces across between the edge of the trees and the reeds which lined the lake. Lestrade showed us the exact spot at which the body had been found, and, indeed, so moist was the ground, that I could plainly see the traces which had been left by the fall of the stricken man. To Holmes, as I could see by his eager face and peering eyes, very many other things were to be read upon the trampled grass. He ran round, like a dog who is picking up a scent, and then turned upon my companion.

"What did you go into the pool for?" he asked.

"I fished about with a rake. I thought there might be some weapon or other trace. But how on earth—"

"Oh, tut, tut! I have no time! That left foot of yours with its inward twist is all over the place. A mole could trace it and there it vanishes among the reeds. Oh, how simple it would all have been had I been here before they came like a herd of buffalo and wallowed all over it. Here is where the party with the lodge-keeper came, and they have covered all tracks for six or eight feet round the body. But here are three separate tracks of the same feet." He

---

contemptuous: disapproving; scornful
conviction: strong belief
reed-girt: surrounded by reeds
pinnacles: the high points of towers
sodden: wet

drew out a lens and lay down upon his waterproof to have a better view, talking all the time rather to himself than to us. "These are young McCarthy's feet. Twice he was walking, and once he ran swiftly, so that the soles are deeply marked and the heels hardly visible. That bears out his story. He ran when he saw his father on the ground. Then here are the father's feet as he paced up and down. What is this, then? It is the butt-end of the gun as the son stood listening. And this? Ha, ha! What have we here? Tiptoes! Tiptoes! Square, too, quite unusual boots! They come, they go, they come again—of course that was for the cloak. Now where did they come from?" He ran up and down, sometimes losing, sometimes finding the track until we were well within the edge of the wood and under the shadow of a great beech, the largest tree in the neighbourhood.

Holmes traced his way to the farther side of this and lay down once more upon his face with a little cry of satisfaction. For a long time he remained there, turning over the leaves and dried sticks, gathering up what seemed to me to be dust into an envelope and examining with his lens not only the ground but even the bark of the tree as far as he could reach. A jagged stone was lying among the moss, and this also he carefully examined and retained. Then he followed a pathway through the wood until he came to the high-road, where all traces were lost.

"It has been a case of considerable interest," he remarked, returning to his natural manner. "I fancy that this gray house on the right must be the lodge. I think that I will go in and have a word with Moran, and perhaps write a little note. Having done that, we may drive back to our luncheon. You may walk to the cab, and I shall be with you presently."

It was about ten minutes before we regained our cab and drove back into Ross, Holmes still carrying with him the stone which he had picked up in the woods.

"This may interest you, Lestrade," he remarked, holding it out. "The murder was done with it."

---

lens: magnifying glass
waterproof: raincoat
highroad: main road

"I see no marks."

"There are none."

"How do you know, then?"

"The grass was growing under it. It had only lain there a few days. There was no sign of a place whence it had been taken. It corresponds with the injuries. There is no sign of any other weapon."

"And the murderer?"

"Is a tall man, left-handed, limps with the right leg, wears thick-soled shooting boots and a gray cloak, smokes Indian cigars, uses a cigar-holder, and carries a blunt pen-knife in his pocket. There are several other indications, but these may be enough to aid us in our search."

Lestrade laughed. "I am afraid that I am still a sceptic," he said. Theories are all very well, but we have to deal with a hard-headed British jury."

"*Nous verrons*," answered Holmes calmly. "You work your own method, and I shall work mine. I shall be busy this afternoon, and shall probably return to London by the evening train."

"And leave your case unfinished?"

"No, finished."

"But the mystery?"

"It is solved."

"Who was the criminal, then?"

"The gentleman I describe."

"But who is he?"

"Surely it would not be difficult to find out. This is not such a populous neighbourhood."

Lestrade shrugged his shoulders. "I am a practical man," he said, "and I really cannot undertake to go about the country looking for a left-handed gentleman with a game-leg. I should become the laughing-stock of Scotland Yard."

---

sceptic: one who is doubtful or disbelieving
Nous verrons: French for "We'll see"
game: lame

"All right," said Holmes quietly. "I have given you the chance. Here are your lodgings. Good-bye. I shall drop you a line before I leave."

Having left Lestrade at his rooms, we drove to our hotel, where we found lunch upon the table. Holmes was silent and buried in thought with a pained expression upon his face, as one who finds himself in a perplexing position.

"Look here, Watson," he said when the cloth was cleared; "just sit down in this chair and let me preach to you for a little. I don't know quite what to do, and I should value your advice. Light a cigar and let me expound."

"Pray do so."

"Well, now, in considering this case there are two points about young McCarthy's narrative which struck us both instantly, although they impressed me in his favour and you against him. One was the fact that his father should, according to his account, cry 'Cooee!' before seeing him. The other was his singular dying reference to a rat. He mumbled several words, you understand, but that was all that caught the son's ear. Now from this double point our research must commence, and we will begin it by presuming that what the lad says is absolutely true."

"What of this 'Cooee!' then?"

"Well, obviously it could not have been meant for the son. The son, as far as he knew, was in Bristol. It was mere chance that he was within earshot. The 'Cooee!' was meant to attract the attention of whoever it was that he had the appointment with. But 'Cooee!' is a distinctly Australian cry, and one which is used between Australians. There is a strong presumption that the person whom McCarthy expected to meet him at Boscombe Pool was someone who had been in Australia. "

"What of the rat, then?"

Sherlock Holmes took a folded paper from his pocket and flattened it out on the table. "This is a map of the Colony of Victoria," he said. "I wired to Bristol for it last night." He put his hand over part of the map. "What do you read?"

"ARAT," I read.

---

expound: explain at length

"And now?" He raised his hand.

"BALLARAT."

"Quite so. That was the word the man uttered, and of which his son only caught the last two syllables. He was trying to utter the name of his murderer. So and so, of Ballarat."

"It is wonderful!" I exclaimed.

"It is obvious. And now, you see, I had narrowed the field down considerably. The possession of a gray garment was a third point which, granting the son's statement to be correct, was a certainty. We have come now out of mere vagueness to the definite conception of an Australian from Ballarat with a gray cloak."

"Certainly."

"And one who was at home in the district, for the pool can only be approached by the farm or by the estate, where strangers could hardly wander."

"Quite so."

"Then comes our expedition of today. By an examination of the ground I gained the trifling details which I gave to that imbecile Lestrade, as to the personality of the criminal."

"But how did you gain them?"

"You know my method. It is founded upon the observation of trifles."

"His height I know that you might roughly judge from the length of his stride. His boots, too, might be told from their traces."

"Yes, they were peculiar boots."

"But his lameness?"

"The impression of his right foot was always less distinct than his left. He put less weight upon it. Why? Because he limped—he was lame."

"But his left-handedness."

"You were yourself struck by the nature of the injury as recorded by the surgeon at the inquest. The blow was struck from immediately behind, and yet was upon the left side. Now, how can that be unless it were by a left-handed man? He had stood behind that tree during the interview between the father and son. He had

---

Ballarat: a city in Victoria, Australia
trifling: minor

even smoked there. I found the ash of a cigar, which my special knowledge of tobacco ashes enables me to pronounce as an Indian cigar. I have, as you know, devoted some attention to this, and written a little monograph on the ashes of 140 different varieties of pipe, cigar, and cigarette tobacco. Having found the ash, I then looked round and discovered the stump among the moss where he had tossed it. It was an Indian cigar, of the variety which are rolled in Rotterdam."

"And the cigar-holder?"

"I could see that the end had not been in his mouth. Therefore he used a holder. The tip had been cut off, but the cut was not a clean one, so I deduced a blunt pen-knife."

"Holmes," I said, "you have drawn a net round this man from which he cannot escape, and you have saved an innocent human life as truly as if you had cut the cord which was hanging him. I see the direction in which all this points. The culprit is—"

"Mr. John Turner," cried the hotel waiter, opening the door of our sitting-room, and ushering in a visitor.

The man who entered was a strange and impressive figure. His slow, limping step and bowed shoulders gave the appearance of decrepitude, and yet his hard, deep-lined, craggy features, and his enormous limbs showed that he was possessed of unusual strength of body and character. His tangled beard, grizzled hair, and outstanding, drooping eyebrows combined to give an air of dignity and power to his appearance, but his face was of an ashen white, while his lips and the corners of his nostrils were tinged with a shade of blue. It was clear to me at a glance that he was in the grip of some deadly and chronic disease.

"Pray sit down on the sofa," said Holmes gently. "You had my note?"

"Yes, the lodge-keeper brought it up. You said that you wished to see me here to avoid scandal."

"I thought people would talk if I went to the Hall."

---

monograph: a scholarly essay or book
Rotterdam: a large city in Holland
decrepitude: a lack of physical strength; feebleness

"And why did you wish to see me?" He looked across at my companion with despair in his weary eyes, as though his question was already answered.

"Yes," said Holmes, answering the look rather than the words. "It is so. I know all about McCarthy."

The old man sank his face in his hands. "God help me!" he cried. "But I would not have let the young man come to harm. I give you my word that I would have spoken out if it went against him at the Assizes."

"I am glad to hear you say so," said Holmes gravely.

"I would have spoken now had it not been for my dear girl. It would break her heart—it will break her heart when she hears that I am arrested."

"It may not come to that," said Holmes.

"What?"

"I am no official agent. I understand that it was your daughter who required my presence here, and I am acting in her interests. Young McCarthy must be got off, however."

"I am a dying man," said old Turner. "I have had diabetes for years. My doctor says it is a question whether I shall live a month. Yet I would rather die under my own roof than in a jail."

Holmes rose and sat down at the table with his pen in his hand and a bundle of paper before him. "Just tell us the truth," he said. "I shall jot down the facts. You will sign it, and Watson here can witness it. Then I could produce your confession at the last extremity to save young McCarthy. I promise you that I shall not use it unless it is absolutely needed."

"It's as well," said the old man; "it's a question whether I shall live to the Assizes, so it matters little to me, but I should wish to spare Alice the shock. And now I will make the thing clear to you; it has been a long time in the acting but will not take me long to tell."

"You didn't know this dead man, McCarthy. He was a devil incarnate. I tell you that. God keep you out of the clutches of such a man as he. His grip has been upon me these twenty years, and he has blasted my life. I'll tell you first how I came to be in his power.

incarnate: in bodily form; made of flesh
blasted: ruined

"It was in the early '60's at the diggings. I was a young chap then, hot-blooded and reckless, ready to turn my hand at anything; I got among bad companions, took to drink, had no luck with my claim, took to the bush, and in a word became what you would call over here a highway robber. There were six of us, and we had a wild, free life of it, sticking up a station from time to time, or stopping the wagons on the road to the diggings. Black Jack of Ballarat was the name I went under, and our party is still remembered in the colony as the Ballarat Gang.

"One day a gold convoy came down from Ballarat to Melbourne, and we lay in wait for it and attacked it. There were six troopers and six of us, so it was a close thing, but we emptied four of their saddles at the first volley. Three of our boys were killed, however, before we got the swag. I put my pistol to the head of the wagon-driver, who was this very man McCarthy. I wish to the Lord that I had shot him then, but I spared him, though I saw his wicked little eyes fixed on my face, as though to remember every feature. We got away with the gold, became wealthy men, and made our way over to England without being suspected. There I parted from my old pals and determined to settle down to a quiet and respectable life. I bought this estate, which chanced to be in the market, and I set myself to do a little good with my money, to make up for the way in which I had earned it. I married, too, and though my wife died young she left me my dear little Alice. Even when she was just a baby her wee hand seemed to lead me down the right path as nothing else had ever done. In a word, I turned over a new leaf and did my best to make up for the past. All was going well when McCarthy laid his grip upon me.

"I had gone up to town about an investment, and I met him in Regent Street with hardly a coat to his back or a boot to his foot.

"'Here we are, Jack,' says he, touching me on the arm; 'we'll be as good as a family to you. There's two of us, me and my son, and you can have the keeping of us. If you don't—it's a fine,

---

diggings: the gold mines
the bush: the wilderness; the backwoods
convoy: a procession of wagons
volley: round of shots
swag: stolen goods

law-abiding country is England, and there's always a policeman within hail.'

"Well, down they came to the west country, there was no shaking them off, and there they have lived rent free on my best land ever since. There was no rest for me, no peace, no forgetfulness; turn where I would, there was his cunning, grinning face at my elbow. It grew worse as Alice grew up, for he soon saw I was more afraid of her knowing my past than of the police. Whatever he wanted he must have, and whatever it was I gave him without question, land, money, houses, until at last he asked a thing which I could not give. He asked for Alice.

"His son, you see, had grown up, and so had my girl, and as I was known to be in weak health, it seemed a fine stroke to him that his lad should step into the whole property. But there I was firm. I would not have his cursed stock mixed with mine; not that I had any dislike to the lad, but his blood was in him, and that was enough. I stood firm. McCarthy threatened. I braved him to do his worst. We were to meet at the pool midway between our houses to talk it over.

"When I went down there I found him talking with his son, so I smoked a cigar and waited behind a tree until he should be alone. But as I listened to his talk all that was black and bitter in me seemed to come uppermost. He was urging his son to marry my daughter with as little regard for what she might think as if she were a slut from off the streets. It drove me mad to think that I and all that I held most dear should be in the power of such a man as this. Could I not snap the bond? I was already a dying and desperate man. Though clear of mind and fairly strong of limb, I knew that my own fate was sealed. But my memory and my girl! Both could be saved if I could but silence that foul tongue. I did it, Mr. Holmes. I would do it again. Deeply as I have sinned, I have led a life of martyrdom to atone for it. But that my girl should be entangled in the same meshes which held me was more than I could suffer. I struck him down with no more compunction than

---

within hail: close enough to call
martyrdom: intense suffering
atone: repent; make amends
compunction: regret or hesitation

if he had been some foul and venomous beast. His cry brought back his son; but I had gained the cover of the wood, though I was forced to go back to fetch the cloak which I had dropped in my flight. That is the true story, gentlemen, of all that occurred."

"Well, it is not for me to judge you," said Holmes as the old man signed the statement which had been drawn out. "I pray that we may never be exposed to such a temptation."

"And what do you intend to do?"

"In view of your health, nothing. You are yourself aware that you will soon have to answer for your deed at a higher court than the Assizes. I will keep your confession, and if McCarthy is condemned I shall be forced to use it. If not, it shall never be seen by mortal eye; and your secret, whether you be alive or dead, shall be safe with us."

"Farewell, then," said the old man solemnly. "Your own death-beds, when they come, will be the easier for the thought of the peace which you have given to mine." Tottering and shaking in all his giant frame, he stumbled slowly from the room.

"God help us!" said Holmes after a long silence. "Why does fate play such tricks with poor, helpless worms? I never hear of such a case as this that I do not think of Baxter's words, and say, 'There, but for the grace of God, goes Sherlock Holmes.'"

James McCarthy was acquitted at the Assizes on the strength of a number of objections which had been drawn out by Holmes and submitted to the defending counsel. Old Turner lived for seven months after our interview, but he is now dead; and there is every prospect that the son and daughter may come to live happily together in ignorance of the black cloud which rests upon their past.

---

tottering: wobbling
Baxter: Richard Baxter, a nineteenth-century English church leader and theologian
acquitted: declared not guilty of specific criminal charges

128

CHALLENGES AND TURNING POINTS

EVELINE

James Joyce

As a young man, James Joyce (1882–1941) left the city of his birth, Dublin, Ireland. But throughout his career, Joyce continued to set his writings—including the radically experimental novel Ulysses *(1922)—in his native city. "Eveline" is from his 1914 collection of stories,* Dubliners.

She sat at the window watching the evening invade the avenue. Her head was leaned against the window curtains and in her nostrils was the odour of dusty cretonne. She was tired.

Few people passed. The man out of the last house passed on his way home; she heard his footsteps clacking along the concrete pavement and afterwards crunching on the cinder path before the new red houses. One time there used to be a field there in which they used to play every evening with other people's children. Then a man from Belfast bought the field and built houses in it—not like their little brown houses but bright brick houses with shining roofs. The children of the avenue used to play together in that field—the Devines, the Waters, the Dunns, little Keogh the cripple, she and her brothers and sisters. Ernest, however, never played: he was too grown up. Her father used often to hunt them in out of the field with his blackthorn stick; but usually little Keogh used to keep *nix* and call out when he saw her father coming. Still they seemed to have been rather happy then. Her father was not so bad then; and besides, her mother was alive. That was a long time ago; she and her brothers and sisters were all grown up; her mother was dead. Tizzie Dunn was dead, too, and the Waters had gone back to

---

cretonne: a strong, heavy fabric
cinder: pebble
Belfast: the largest city in Northern Ireland
blackthorn stick: a walking stick
nix: guard

England. Everything changes. Now she was going to go away like the others, to leave her home.

Home! She looked round the room, reviewing all its familiar objects which she had dusted once a week for so many years, wondering where on earth all the dust came from. Perhaps she would never see again those familiar objects from which she had never dreamed of being divided. And yet during all those years she had never found out the name of the priest whose yellowing photograph hung on the wall above the broken harmonium beside the coloured print of the promises made to Blessed Margaret Mary Alacoque. He had been a school friend of her father. Whenever he showed the photograph to a visitor her father used to pass it with a casual word:

—He is in Melbourne now.

She had consented to go away, to leave her home. Was that wise? She tried to weigh each side of the question. In her home anyway she had shelter and food; she had those whom she had known all her life about her. Of course she had to work hard both in the house and at business. What would they say of her in the Stores when they found out that she had run away with a fellow? Say she was a fool, perhaps; and her place would be filled up by advertisement. Miss Gavan would be glad. She had always had an edge on her, especially whenever there were people listening.

—Miss Hill, don't you see these ladies are waiting?

—Look lively, Miss Hill, please.

She would not cry many tears at leaving the Stores.

But in her new home, in a distant unknown country, it would not be like that. Then she would be married—she, Eveline. People would treat her with respect then. She would not be treated as her mother had been. Even now, though she was over nineteen, she sometimes felt herself in danger of her father's violence. She knew it was that that had given her the palpitations. When they were growing up he had never gone for her, like he used to go for

harmonium: a musical instrument similar to a small organ
Blessed Margaret Mary Alacoque: a seventeenth-century French saint
Melbourne: a large city in Australia
in the Stores: in the store where Eveline works
the palpitations: rapid, irregular beating of the heart

Harry and Ernest, because she was a girl; but latterly he had begun to threaten her and say what he would do to her only for her dead mother's sake. And now she had nobody to protect her. Ernest was dead and Harry, who was in the church decorating business, was nearly always down somewhere in the country. Besides, the invariable squabble for money on Saturday nights had begun to weary her unspeakably. She always gave her entire wages—seven shillings—and Harry always sent up what he could but the trouble was to get any money from her father. He said she used to squander the money, that she had no head, that he wasn't going to give her his hard-earned money to throw about the streets, and much more, for he was usually fairly bad of a Saturday night. In the end he would give her the money and ask her had she any intention of buying Sunday's dinner. Then she had to rush out as quickly as she could and do her marketing, holding her black leather purse tightly in her hand as she elbowed her way through the crowds and returning home late under her load of provisions. She had hard work to keep the house together and to see that the two young children who had been left to her charge went to school regularly and got their meals regularly. It was hard work—a hard life—but now that she was about to leave it she did not find it a wholly undesirable life.

She was about to explore another life with Frank. Frank was very kind, manly, open-hearted. She was to go away with him by the night-boat to be his wife and to live with him in Buenos Aires where he had a home waiting for her. How well she remembered the first time she had seen him; he was lodging in a house on the main road where she used to visit. It seemed a few weeks ago. He was standing at the gate, his peaked cap pushed back on his head

---

latterly: recently
invariable: usual; unchanging
seven shillings: a relatively small amount of money
squander: waste
fairly bad: rather drunk
provisions: food and supplies
the night-boat: the evening ferry to Liverpool, England, from where ships set out
    for longer journeys
Buenos Aires: the capital of Argentina, in South America
peaked cap: a hat with a round top and a flat visor, like those often worn by police
    officers and soldiers

and his hair tumbled forward over a face of bronze. Then they had come to know each other. He used to meet her outside the Stores every evening and see her home. He took her to see *The Bohemian Girl* and she felt elated as she sat in an unaccustomed part of the theatre with him. He was awfully fond of music and sang a little. People knew that they were courting and, when he sang about the lass that loves a sailor, she always felt pleasantly confused. He used to call her Poppens out of fun. First of all it had been an excitement for her to have a fellow and then she had begun to like him. He had tales of distant countries. He had started as a deck boy at a pound a month on a ship of the Allan Line going out to Canada. He told her the names of the ships he had been on and the names of the different services. He had sailed through the Straits of Magellan and he told her stories of the terrible Patagonians. He had fallen on his feet in Buenos Aires, he said, and had come over to the old country just for a holiday. Of course, her father had found out the affair and had forbidden her to have anything to say to him.

—I know these sailor chaps, he said.

One day he had quarrelled with Frank and after that she had to meet her lover secretly.

The evening deepened in the avenue. The white of two letters in her lap grew indistinct. One was to Harry; the other was to her father. Ernest had been her favourite but she liked Harry too. Her father was becoming old lately, she noticed; he would miss her. Sometimes he could be very nice. Not long before, when she had been laid up for a day, he had read her out a ghost story and made toast for her at the fire. Another day, when their mother was alive,

---

The Bohemian Girl: a popular nineteenth-century opera
elated: extremely happy
lass: young girl
Allan Line: a shipping line with boats that traveled from Liverpool, England, to the west coast of North America by sailing around the southern tip of South America
Straits of Magellan: a South American waterway that serves as a natural passage from the Atlantic to the Pacific Ocean through the southern tip of Chile
Patagonians: people from the Patagonia region of South America who, according to some European legends, were fierce giants
indistinct: blurry; unclear

they had all gone for a picnic to the Hill of Howth. She remembered her father putting on her mother's bonnet to make the children laugh.

Her time was running out but she continued to sit by the window, leaning her head against the window curtain, inhaling the odour of dusty cretonne. Down far in the avenue she could hear a street organ playing. She knew the air. Strange that it should come that very night to remind her of the promise to her mother, her promise to keep the home together as long as she could. She remembered the last night of her mother's illness; she was again in the close dark room at the other side of the hall and outside she heard a melancholy air of Italy. The organ-player had been ordered to go away and given sixpence. She remembered her father strutting back into the sickroom saying:

—Damned Italians! coming over here!

As she mused the pitiful vision of her mother's life laid its spell on the very quick of her being—that life of commonplace sacrifices closing in final craziness. She trembled as she heard again her mother's voice saying constantly with foolish insistence:

—Derevaun Seraun! Derevaun Seraun!

She stood up in a sudden impulse of terror. Escape! She must escape! Frank would save her. He would give her life, perhaps love, too. But she wanted to live. Why should she be unhappy? She had a right to happiness. Frank would take her in his arms, fold her in his arms. He would save her.

• • •

She stood among the swaying crowd in the station at the North Wall. He held her hand and she knew that he was speaking to her, saying something about the passage over and over again. The

---

Hill of Howth: a hill on a coastal peninsula just north of the city of Dublin
air: melody; song
sixpence: a small amount of money; loose change
mused: contemplated
Derevaun Seraun: the meaning is uncertain, though some scholars think it might be a garbled form of an old phrase meaning "the end of pleasure is pain"
the North Wall: a dock on the north bank of the River Liffey in Dublin, from which ferries departed

station was full of soldiers with brown baggages. Through the wide doors of the sheds she caught a glimpse of the black mass of the boat, lying in beside the quay wall, with illumined portholes. She answered nothing. She felt her cheek pale and cold and, out of a maze of distress, she prayed to God to direct her, to show her what was her duty. The boat blew a long mournful whistle into the mist. If she went, to-morrow she would be on the sea with Frank, steaming toward Buenos Aires. Their passage had been booked. Could she still draw back after all he had done for her? Her distress awoke a nausea in her body and she kept moving her lips in silent fervent prayer.

A bell clanged upon her heart. She felt him seize her hand:

—Come!

All the seas of the world tumbled about her heart. He was drawing her into them: he would drown her. She gripped with both hands at the iron railing.

—Come!

No! No! No! It was impossible. Her hands clutched the iron in frenzy. Amid the seas she sent a cry of anguish!

—Eveline! Evvy!

He rushed beyond the barrier and called to her to follow. He was shouted at to go on but he still called to her. She set her white face to him, passive, like a helpless animal. Her eyes gave him no sign of love or farewell or recognition.

---

quay: a wharf on a riverside
illumined: lit
fervent: passionate
passive: inactive

THE ROCKING-HORSE WINNER

D.H. Lawrence

D.H. (David Herbert) Lawrence (1885–1930), born the son of an English coal miner, became one of the most prolific, controversial, and influential British writers of the early twentieth century. His writings often dramatized the influence of powerful instincts and unconscious desires on human behavior. "The Rocking-Horse Winner" was first published in 1926.

There was a woman who was beautiful, who started with all the advantages, yet she had no luck. She married for love, and the love turned to dust. She had bonny children, yet she felt they had been thrust upon her, and she could not love them. They looked at her coldly, as if they were finding fault with her. And hurriedly she felt she must cover up some fault in herself. Yet what it was that she must cover up she never knew. Nevertheless, when her children were present, she always felt the center of her heart go hard. This troubled her, and in her manner she was all the more gentle and anxious for her children, as if she loved them very much. Only she herself knew that at the center of her heart was a hard little place that could not feel love, no, not for anybody. Everybody else said of her: "She is such a good mother. She adores her children." Only she herself, and her children themselves, knew it was not so. They read it in each other's eyes.

There were a boy and two little girls. They lived in a pleasant house, with a garden, and they had discreet servants, and felt themselves superior to anyone in the neighborhood.

Although they lived in style, they felt always an anxiety in the house. There was never enough money. The mother had a small income, and the father had a small income, but not nearly enough

---

bonny: pleasant; attractive
discreet: tactful; reserved

for the social position which they had to keep up. The father went in to town to some office. But though he had good prospects, these prospects never materialized. There was always the grinding sense of the shortage of money, though the style was always kept up.

At last the mother said: "I will see if *I* can't make something." But she did not know where to begin. She racked her brains, and tried this thing and the other, but could not find anything successful. The failure made deep lines come into her face. Her children were growing up, they would have to go to school. There must be more money, there must be more money. The father, who was always very handsome and expensive in his tastes, seemed as if he never *would* be able to do anything worth doing. And the mother, who had a great belief in herself, did not succeed any better, and her tastes were just as expensive.

And so the house came to be haunted by the unspoken phrase: *There must be more money! There must be more money!* The children could hear it all the time, though nobody said it aloud. They heard it at Christmas, when the expensive and splendid toys filled the nursery. Behind the shining modern rocking-horse, behind the smart doll's house, a voice would start whispering: "There *must* be more money! There *must* be more money!" And the children would stop playing, to listen for a moment. They would look into each other's eyes, to see if they had all heard. And each one saw in the eyes of the other two that they too had heard. "There *must* be more money! There *must* be more money!"

It came whispering from the springs of the still-swaying rocking-horse, and even the horse, bending his wooden, champing head, heard it. The big doll, sitting so pink and smirking in her new pram, could hear it quite plainly, and seemed to be smirking all the more self-consciously because of it. The foolish puppy, too, that took the place of the teddy-bear, he was looking so extraordinarily foolish for no other reason but that he heard the secret whisper all over the house: "There *must* be more money!"

---

prospects: opportunities
materialized: became reality
champing: bobbing; moving as though chomping on something
pram: stroller

Yet nobody ever said it aloud. The whisper was everywhere, and therefore no one spoke it. Just as no one ever says: "We are breathing!" in spite of the fact that breath is coming and going all the time.

"Mother," said the boy Paul one day, "why don't we keep a car of our own? Why do we always use uncle's, or else a taxi?"

"Because we're the poor members of the family," said the mother.

"But why *are* we, mother?"

"Well—I suppose," she said slowly and bitterly, "it's because your father has no luck."

The boy was silent for some time.

"Is luck money, mother?" he asked rather timidly.

"No, Paul. Not quite. It's what causes you to have money."

"Oh!" said Paul vaguely. "I thought when Uncle Oscar said *filthy lucker*, it meant money."

"*Filthy lucre* does mean money," said the mother. "But it's lucre, not luck."

"Oh!" said the boy. "Then what *is* luck, mother?"

"It's what causes you to have money. If you're lucky you have money. That's why it's better to be born lucky than rich. If you're rich, you may lose your money. But if you're lucky, you will always get more money."

"Oh! Will you? And is father not lucky?"

"Very unlucky, I should say," she said bitterly.

The boy watched her with unsure eyes.

"Why?" he asked.

"I don't know. Nobody ever knows why one person is lucky and another unlucky."

"Don't they? Nobody at all? Does *nobody* know?"

"Perhaps God. But He never tells."

"He ought to, then. And aren't you lucky either, mother?"

"I can't be, if I married an unlucky husband."

"But by yourself, aren't you?"

"I used to think I was, before I married. Now I think I am very unlucky indeed."

---

lucre: riches

"Why?"

"Well—never mind! Perhaps I'm not really," she said.

The child looked at her, to see if she meant it. But he saw, by the lines of her mouth, that she was only trying to hide something from him.

"Well, anyhow," he said stoutly, "I'm a lucky person."

"Why?" said his mother, with a sudden laugh.

He stared at her. He didn't even know why he had said it.

"God told me," he asserted, brazening it out.

"I hope He did, dear!" she said, again with a laugh, but rather bitter.

"He did, mother!"

"Excellent!" said the mother, using one of her husband's exclamations.

The boy saw she did not believe him; or, rather, that she paid no attention to his assertion. This angered him somewhat, and made him want to compel her attention.

He went off by himself, vaguely, in a childish way, seeking for the clue to "luck." Absorbed, taking no heed of other people, he went about with a sort of stealth, seeking inwardly for luck. He wanted luck, he wanted it, he wanted it. When the two girls were playing dolls in the nursery, he would sit on his big rocking-horse, charging madly into space, with a frenzy that made the little girls peer at him uneasily. Wildly the horse careered, the waving dark hair of the boy tossed, his eyes had a strange glare in them. The little girls dared not speak to him.

When he had ridden to the end of his mad little journey, he climbed down and stood in front of his rocking-horse, staring fixedly into its lowered face. Its red mouth was slightly open, its big eye was wide and glassy-bright.

"Now!" he would silently command the snorting steed. "Now, take me to where there is luck! Now take me!"

---

stoutly: firmly; with conviction
brazening it out: becoming even bolder
compel: force
stealth: sneakiness
careered: moved forward quickly and headfirst
steed: horse

And he would slash the horse on the neck with the little whip he had asked Uncle Oscar for. He *knew* the horse could take him to where there was luck, if only he forced it. So he would mount again, and start on his furious ride, hoping at last to get there. He knew he could get there.

"You'll break your horse, Paul!" said the nurse.

"He's always riding like that! I wish he'd leave off!" said his elder sister Joan.

But he only glared down on them in silence. Nurse gave him up. She could make nothing of him. Anyhow he was growing beyond her.

One day his mother and his Uncle Oscar came in when he was on one of his furious rides. He did not speak to them.

"Hallo, you young jockey! Riding a winner?" said his uncle.

"Aren't you growing too big for a rocking-horse? You're not a very little boy any longer, you know," said his mother.

But Paul only gave a blue glare from his big, rather close-set eyes. He would speak to nobody when he was in full tilt. His mother watched him with an anxious expression on her face.

At last he suddenly stopped forcing his horse into the mechanical gallop, and slid down.

"Well, I got there!" he announced fiercely, his blue eyes still flaring, and his sturdy long legs straddling apart.

"Where did you get to?" asked his mother.

"Where I wanted to go," he flared back at her.

"That's right, son!" said Uncle Oscar. "Don't you stop till you get there. What's the horse's name?"

"He doesn't have a name," said the boy.

"Gets on without all right?" asked the uncle.

"Well, he has different names. He was called Sansovino last week."

"Sansovino, eh? Won the Ascot. How did you know his name?"

"He always talks about horse-races with Bassett," said Joan.

---

in full tilt: at top speed
the Ascot: the Ascot Gold Cup, a major horse race in the United Kingdom

The uncle was delighted to find that his small nephew was posted with all the racing news. Bassett, the young gardener, who had been wounded in the left foot in the war and had got his present job through Oscar Cresswell, whose batman he had been, was a perfect blade of the "turf." He lived in the racing events, and the small boy lived with him.

Oscar Cresswell got it all from Bassett.

"Master Paul comes and asks me, so I can't do more than tell him, sir," said Bassett, his face terribly serious, as if he were speaking of religious matters.

"And does he ever put anything on a horse he fancies?"

"Well—I don't want to give him away—he's a young sport, a fine sport, sir. Would you mind asking him himsel? He sort of takes a pleasure in it, and perhaps he'd feel I was giving him away, sir, if you don't mind."

Bassett was serious as a church.

The uncle went back to his nephew and took him off for a ride in the car.

"Say, Paul, old man, do you ever put anything on a horse?" the uncle asked.

The boy watched the handsome man closely.

"Why, do you think I oughtn't to?" he parried.

"Not a bit of it. I thought perhaps you might give me a tip for the Lincoln."

The car sped on into the country, going down to Uncle Oscar's place in Hampshire.

"Honor bright?" said the nephew.

"Honor bright, son!" said the uncle.

"Well, then, Daffodil."

"Daffodil! I doubt it, sonny. What about Mirza?"

"I only know the winner," said the boy. "That's Daffodil."

---

posted: up to date
batman: an orderly or attendant in the military
a perfect blade of the "turf": a stylish fan of horse racing
sport: a likable individual
the Lincoln: the Lincoln Handicap, a major horse race in the United Kingdom
Hampshire: a county on the south coast of England
honor bright: an expression meaning "truly," or "on your honor"

"Daffodil, eh?"

There was a pause. Daffodil was an obscure horse comparatively.

"Uncle!"

"Yes, son?"

"You won't let it go any further, will you? I promised Bassett."

"Bassett be damned, old man! What's he got to do with it?"

"We're partners. We've been partners from the first. Uncle, he lent me my first five shillings, which I lost. I promised him, honor bright, it was only between me and him; only you gave me that ten-shilling note I started winning with, so I thought you were lucky. You won't let it go any further, will you?"

The boy gazed at his uncle from those big, hot, blue eyes, set rather close together. The uncle stirred and laughed uneasily.

"Right you are, son! I'll keep your tip private. Daffodil, eh? How much are you putting on him?"

"All except twenty pounds," said the boy. "I keep that in reserve."

The uncle thought it a good joke.

"You keep twenty pounds in reserve, do you, you young romancer? What are you betting, then?"

"I'm betting three hundred," said the boy gravely. "But it's between you and me, Uncle Oscar! Honor bright?"

The uncle burst into a roar of laughter.

It's between you and me all right, you young Nat Gould," he said, laughing. "But where's your three hundred?"

"Bassett keeps it for me. We're partners."

"You are, are you! And what is Bassett putting on Daffodil?"

"He won't go quite as high as I do, I expect. Perhaps he'll go a hundred and fifty."

---

obscure: little-known

comparatively: in comparison to others

five shillings: a relatively small amount of money

note: a piece of paper money

pounds: the main unit of British currency; 20 pounds is a significant amount for a young boy to have

romancer: tale-teller

gravely: seriously

Nat Gould: a British novelist and journalist, also an editor of various horse-racing newspapers

"What, pennies?" laughed the uncle.

"Pounds," said the child, with a surprised look at his uncle. "Bassett keeps a bigger reserve than I do."

Between wonder and amusement Uncle Oscar was silent. He pursued the matter no further, but he determined to take his nephew with him to the Lincoln races.

"Now, son," he said, "I'm putting twenty on Mirza, and I'll put five for you on any horse you fancy. What's your pick?"

"Daffodil, uncle."

"No, not the fiver on Daffodil!"

"I should if it was my own fiver," said the child.

"Good! Good! Right you are! A fiver for me and a fiver for you on Daffodil."

The child had never been to a race-meeting before, and his eyes were blue fire. He pursed his mouth tight, and watched. A Frenchman just in front had put his money on Lancelot. Wild with excitement, he flayed his arms up and down, yelling, "*Lancelot! Lancelot!*" in his French accent.

Daffodil came in first, Lancelot second, Mirza third. The child, flushed and with eyes blazing, was curiously serene. His uncle brought him four five-pound notes, four to one.

"What am I to do with these?" he cried, waving them before the boy's eyes.

"I suppose we'll talk to Bassett," said the boy. "I expect I have fifteen hundred now; and twenty in reserve; and this twenty."

His uncle studied him for some moments.

"Look here, son!" he said. "You're not serious about Bassett and that fifteen hundred, are you?"

"Yes, I am. But it's between you and me, uncle. Honor bright!"

"Honor bright all right, son! But I must talk to Bassett."

"If you'd like to be a partner, uncle, with Bassett and me, we could all be partners. Only, you'd have to promise, honor bright, uncle, not to let it go beyond us three. Bassett and I are lucky,

---

pursed: puckered
flushed: red in the face
serene: calm

143

and you must be lucky, because it was your ten shillings I started winning with...."

Uncle Oscar took both Bassett and Paul into Richmond Park for an afternoon, and there they talked.

"It's like this, you see, sir," Bassett said. "Master Paul would get me talking about racing events, spinning yarns, you know, sir. And he was always keen on knowing if I'd made or if I'd lost. It's about a year since, now, that I put five shillings on Blush of Dawn for him—and we lost. Then the luck turned, and with that ten shillings he had from you, that we put on Singhalese. And since that time, it's been pretty steady, all things considering. What do you say, Master Paul?"

"We're all right when we're sure," said Paul. "It's when we're not quite sure that we go down."

"Oh, but we're careful then," said Bassett.

"But when are you *sure?*" smiled Uncle Oscar.

"It's Master Paul, sir," said Bassett, in a secret, religious voice. "It's as if he had it from heaven. Like Daffodil, now, for the Lincoln. That was as sure as eggs."

"Did you put anything on Daffodil?" asked Oscar Cresswell.

"Yes, sir. I made my bit."

"And my nephew?"

Bassett was obstinately silent, looking at Paul.

"I made twelve hundred, didn't I, Bassett? I told uncle I was putting three hundred on Daffodil."

"That's right," said Bassett, nodding.

"But where's the money?" asked the uncle.

"I keep it safe locked up, sir. Master Paul he can have it any minute he likes to ask for it."

"What, fifteen hundred pounds?"

"And twenty! And *forty*, that is, with the twenty he made on the course."

"It's amazing!" said the uncle.

Richmond Park: the largest park in London
spinning yarns: telling stories
as sure as eggs: absolutely certain
obstinately: stubbornly

"If Master Paul offers you to be partners, sir, I would, if I were you; if you'll excuse me," said Bassett.

Oscar Cresswell thought about it.

"I'll see the money," he said.

They drove home again, and sure enough, Bassett came round to the garden-house with fifteen hundred pounds in notes. The twenty pounds reserve was left with Joe Glee, in the Turf Commission deposit.

"You see, it's all right, uncle, when I'm *sure!* Then we go strong, for all we're worth. Don't we, Bassett?"

"We do that, Master Paul."

"And when are you sure?" said the uncle, laughing.

"Oh, well, sometimes I'm *absolutely* sure, like about Daffodil," said the boy; "and sometimes I have an idea; and sometimes I haven't even an idea, have I, Bassett? Then we're careful, because we mostly go down."

"You do, do you! And when you're sure, like about Daffodil, what makes you sure, sonny?"

"Oh, well, I don't know," said the boy uneasily. "I'm sure, you know, uncle; that's all."

"It's as if he had it from heaven, sir," Bassett reiterated.

"I should say so!" said the uncle.

But he became a partner. And when the Leger was coming on, Paul was "sure" about Lively Spark, which was a quite inconsiderable horse. The boy insisted on putting a thousand on the horse, Bassett went for five hundred, and Oscar Cresswell two hundred. Lively Spark came in first, and the betting had been ten to one against him. Paul had made ten thousand.

"You see," he said, "I was absolutely sure of him."

Even Oscar Cresswell had cleared two thousand.

"Look here, son," he said, "this sort of thing makes me nervous."

"It needn't, uncle! Perhaps I shan't be sure again for a long time."

Turf Commission deposit: an office at a racecourse where money can be deposited
the Leger: the St. Leger Stakes, a major horse race in the United Kingdom
inconsiderable: unimpressive

"But what are you going to do with your money?" asked the uncle.

"Of course," said the boy, "I started it for mother. She said she had no luck, because father is unlucky, so I thought if *I* was lucky, it might stop whispering."

"What might stop whispering?"

"Our house. I *hate* our house for whispering."

"What does it whisper?"

"Why—why"—the boy fidgeted—"why, I don't know. But it's always short of money, you know, uncle."

"I know it, son, I know it."

"You know people send mother writs, don't you, uncle?"

"I'm afraid I do," said the uncle.

"And then the house whispers, like people laughing at you behind your back. It's awful, that is! I thought if I was lucky..."

"You might stop it," added the uncle.

The boy watched him with big blue eyes, that had an uncanny cold fire in them, and he said never a word.

"Well, then!" said the uncle. "What are we doing?"

"I shouldn't like mother to know I was lucky," said the boy.

"Why not, son?"

"She'd stop me."

"I don't think she would."

"Oh!"—and the boy writhed in an odd way—"I *don't* want her to know, uncle."

"All right, son! We'll manage it without her knowing."

They managed it very easily. Paul, at the other's suggestion, handed over five thousand pounds to his uncle, who deposited it with the family lawyer, who was then to inform Paul's mother that a relative had put five thousand pounds into his hands, which sum was to be paid out a thousand pounds at a time, on the mother's birthday, for the next five years.

---

writs: legal orders, issued by a court, to pay a debt
uncanny: strange
writhed: twisted

"So she'll have a birthday present of a thousand pounds for five successive years," said Uncle Oscar. "I hope it won't make it all the harder for her later."

Paul's mother had her birthday in November. The house had been "whispering" worse than ever lately, and, even in spite of his luck, Paul could not bear up against it. He was very anxious to see the effect of the birthday letter, telling his mother about the thousand pounds.

When there were no visitors, Paul now took his meals with his parents, as he was beyond the nursery control. His mother went into town nearly every day. She had discovered that she had an odd knack of sketching furs and dress materials, so she worked secretly in the studio of a friend who was the chief "artist" for the leading drapers. She drew the figures of ladies in furs and ladies in silk and sequins for the newspaper advertisements. This young woman artist earned several thousand pounds a year, but Paul's mother only made several hundreds, and she was again dissatisfied. She so wanted to be first in something, and she did not succeed, even in making sketches for drapery advertisements.

She was down to breakfast on the morning of her birthday. Paul watched her face as she read the letters. He knew the lawyer's letter. As his mother read it, her face hardened and became more expressionless. Then a cold, determined look came on her mouth. She hid the letter under the pile of others, and said not a word about it.

"Didn't you have anything nice in the post for your birthday, mother?" said Paul.

"Quite moderately nice," she said, her voice cold and absent.

She went away to town without saying more.

But in the afternoon Uncle Oscar appeared. He said Paul's mother had had a long interview with the lawyer, asking if the whole five thousand could not be advanced at once, as she was in debt.

"What do you think, uncle?" said the boy.

"I leave it to you, son."

---

drapers: makers and sellers of clothes

"Oh, let her have it, then! We can get some more with the other," said the boy.

"A bird in the hand is worth two in the bush, laddie!" said Uncle Oscar.

"But I'm sure to *know* for the Grand National; or the Lincolnshire; or else the Derby. I'm sure to know for *one* of them," said Paul.

So Uncle Oscar signed the agreement, and Paul's mother touched the whole five thousand. Then something very curious happened. The voices in the house suddenly went mad, like a chorus of frogs on a spring evening. There were certain new furnishings, and Paul had a tutor. He was *really* going to Eton, his father's school, in the following autumn. There were flowers in the winter, and a blossoming of the luxury Paul's mother had been used to. And yet the voices in the house, behind the sprays of mimosa and almond blossom, and from under the piles of iridescent cushions, simply trilled and screamed in a sort of ecstasy: "There *must* be more money! Oh-h-h; there *must* be more money. Oh, now, now-w! Now-w-w—there *must* be more money! —more than ever! More than ever!"

It frightened Paul terribly. He studied away at his Latin and Greek with his tutors. But his intense hours were spent with Bassett. The Grand National had gone by: he had not "known," and had lost a hundred pounds. Summer was at hand. He was in agony for the Lincoln. But even for the Lincoln he didn't "know," and he lost fifty pounds. He became wild-eyed and strange, as if something were going to explode in him.

"Let it alone, son! Don't you bother about it!" urged Uncle Oscar. But it was as if the boy couldn't really hear what his uncle was saying.

---

the Grand National...the Derby: major horse races in the United Kingdom
Eton: a prestigious private school in England
mimosa: a type of tree, herb, or small shrub
iridescent: sparkling
trilled: warbled; sang
ecstasy: overwhelming emotion

"I've got to know for the Derby! I've got to know for the Derby!" the child reiterated, his big blue eyes blazing with a sort of madness.

His mother noticed how overwrought he was.

"You'd better go to the seaside. Wouldn't you like to go now to the seaside, instead of waiting? I think you'd better," she said, looking down at him anxiously, her heart curiously heavy because of him.

But the child lifted his uncanny blue eyes.

"I couldn't possibly go before the Derby, mother!" he said. "I couldn't possibly!"

"Why not?" she said, her voice becoming heavy when she was opposed. "Why not? You can still go from the seaside to see the Derby with your Uncle Oscar, if that's what you wish. No need for you to wait here. Besides, I think you care too much about these races. It's a bad sign. My family has been a gambling family, and you won't know till you grow up how much damage it has done. But it has done damage. I shall have to send Bassett away, and ask Uncle Oscar not to talk racing to you, unless you promise to be reasonable about it; go away to the seaside and forget it. You're all nerves!"

"I'll do what you like, mother, so long as you don't send me away till after the Derby," the boy said.

"Send you away from where? Just from this house?"

"Yes," he said, gazing at her.

"Why, you curious child, what makes you care about this house so much, suddenly? I never knew you loved it."

He gazed at her without speaking. He had a secret within a secret, something he had not divulged, even to Bassett or to his Uncle Oscar.

But his mother, after standing undecided and a little bit sullen for some moments, said:

"Very well, then! Don't go to the seaside till after the Derby, if you don't wish it. But promise me you won't let your nerves go to

reiterated: stated again, with emphasis
overwrought: tense; stressed
divulged: made known; disclosed
sullen: gloomy; grim

pieces. Promise you won't think so much about horse-racing and *events*, as you call them!"

"Oh, no," said the boy casually. "I won't think much about them, mother. You needn't worry. I wouldn't worry, mother, if I were you."

"If you were me and I were you," said his mother, "I wonder what we *should* do!"

"But you know you needn't worry, mother, don't you?" the boy repeated.

"I should be awfully glad to know it," she said wearily.

"Oh, well, you *can*, you know. I mean, you *ought* to know you needn't worry," he insisted.

"Ought I? Then I'll see about it," she said.

Paul's secret of secrets was his wooden horse, that which had no name. Since he was emancipated from a nurse and a nursery-governess, he had had his rocking-horse removed to his own bedroom at the top of the house.

"Surely, you're too big for a rocking-horse!" his mother had remonstrated.

"Well, you see, mother, till I can have a *real* horse, I like to have *some* sort of animal about," had been his quaint answer.

"Do you feel he keeps you company?" she laughed.

"Oh, yes! He's very good, he always keeps me company, when I'm there," said Paul.

So the horse, rather shabby, stood in an arrested prance in the boy's bedroom.

The Derby was drawing near, and the boy grew more and more tense. He hardly heard what was spoken to him, he was very frail, and his eyes were really uncanny. His mother had sudden strange seizures of uneasiness about him. Sometimes, for half-an-hour, she would feel a sudden anxiety about him that was almost anguish. She wanted to rush to him at once, and know he was safe.

Two nights before the Derby, she was at a big party in town, when one of her rushes of anxiety about her boy, her first-born,

---

emancipated: freed
nursery-governess: nanny
remonstrated: protested
quaint: charming; cute

gripped her heart till she could hardly speak. She fought with the feeling, might and main, for she believed in common-sense. But it was too strong. She had to leave the dance and go downstairs to telephone to the country. The children's nursery-governess was terribly surprised and startled at being rung up in the night.

"Are the children all right, Miss Wilmot?"

"Oh, yes, they are quite all right."

"Master Paul? Is he all right?"

"He went to bed as right as a trivet. Shall I run up and look at him?"

"No," said Paul's mother reluctantly. "No! Don't trouble. It's all right. Don't sit up. We shall be home fairly soon." She did not want her son's privacy intruded upon.

"Very good," said the governess.

It was about one o'clock when Paul's mother and father drove up to their house. All was still. Paul's mother went to her room and slipped off her white fur cloak. She had told her maid not to wait up for her. She heard her husband downstairs, mixing a whisky-and-soda.

And then, because of the strange anxiety at her heart, she stole upstairs to her son's room. Noiselessly she went along the upper corridor. Was there a faint noise? What was it?

She stood, with arrested muscles, outside his door, listening. There was a strange, heavy, and yet not loud noise. Her heart stood still. It was a soundless noise, yet rushing and powerful. Something huge, in violent, hushed motion. What was it? What in God's name was it? She ought to know. She felt that she knew the noise. She knew what it was.

Yet she could not place it. She couldn't say what it was. And on and on it went, like a madness.

Softly, frozen with anxiety and fear, she turned the door-handle.

The room was dark. Yet in the space near the window, she heard and saw something plunging to and fro. She gazed in fear and amazement.

---

might and main: with all possible strength
as right as a trivet: an expression meaning "perfectly fine"

Then suddenly she switched on the light, and saw her son, in his green pajamas, madly surging on the rocking-horse. The blaze of light suddenly lit him up, as he urged the wooden horse, and lit her up, as she stood, blonde, in her dress of pale green and crystal, in the doorway.

"Paul!" she cried. "Whatever are you doing?"

"It's Malabar!" he screamed, in a powerful, strange voice. "It's Malabar!"

His eyes blazed at her for one strange and senseless second, as he ceased urging his wooden horse. Then he fell with a crash to the ground, and she, all her tormented motherhood flooding upon her, rushed to gather him up.

But he was unconscious, and unconscious he remained, with some brainfever. He talked and tossed, and his mother sat stonily by his side.

"Malabar! It's Malabar! Bassett, Bassett, I *know*! It's Malabar!"

So the child cried, trying to get up and urge the rocking-horse that gave him his inspiration.

"What does he mean by Malabar?" asked the heart-frozen mother.

"I don't know," said the father stonily.

"What does he mean by Malabar?" she asked her brother Oscar.

"It's one of the horses running for the Derby," was the answer.

And, in spite of himself, Oscar Cresswell spoke to Bassett, and himself put a thousand on Malabar: at fourteen to one.

The third day of the illness was critical: they were waiting for a change. The boy, with his rather long, curly hair, was tossing ceaselessly on the pillow. He neither slept nor regained consciousness, and his eyes were like blue stones. His mother sat, feeling her heart had gone, turned actually into a stone.

In the evening, Oscar Cresswell did not come, but Bassett sent a message, saying could he come up for one moment, just one moment? Paul's mother was very angry at the intrusion, but on second thought she agreed. The boy was the same. Perhaps Bassett might bring him to consciousness.

The gardener, a shortish fellow with a little brown moustache, and sharp little brown eyes, tiptoed into the room, touched his imaginary cap to Paul's mother, and stole to the bedside, staring with glittering, smallish eyes, at the tossing, dying child.

"Master Paul!" he whispered. "Master Paul! Malabar came in first all right, a clean win. I did as you told me. You've made over seventy thousand pounds, you have; you've got over eighty thousand. Malabar came in all right, Master Paul."

"Malabar! Malabar! Did I say Malabar, mother? Did I say Malabar? Do you think I'm lucky, mother? I knew Malabar, didn't I? Over eighty thousand pounds! I call that lucky, don't you, mother? Over eighty thousand pounds! I knew, didn't I know I knew? Malabar came in all right. If I ride my horse till I'm sure, then I tell you, Bassett, you can go as high as you like. Did you go for all you were worth, Bassett?"

"I went a thousand on it, Master Paul."

"I never told you, mother, that if I can ride my horse, and *get there*, then I'm absolutely sure—oh, absolutely! Mother, did I ever tell you? I *am* lucky!"

"No, you never did," said the mother.

But the boy died in the night.

And even as he lay dead, his mother heard her brother's voice saying to her: "My God, Hester, you're eighty-odd thousand to the good, and a poor devil of a son to the bad. But, poor devil, poor devil, he's best gone out of a life where he rides his rocking-horse to find a winner."

THE TRAIN FROM RHODESIA

Nadine Gordimer

The South African author Nadine Gordimer (born in 1923) won the Nobel Prize in Literature in 1991. "The Train from Rhodesia," one of her earliest stories, was first published in her 1952 collection, The Soft Voice of the Serpent and Other Stories. *Rhodesia, once a British colony in south-central Africa, has since become the independent nations of Zambia and Zimbabwe.*

The train came out of the red horizon and bore down toward them over the single straight track.

The stationmaster came out of his little brick station with its pointed chalet roof, feeling the creases in his serge uniform in his legs as well. A stir of preparedness rippled through the squatting native vendors waiting in the dust; the face of a carved wooden animal, eternally surprised, stuck out of a sack. The stationmaster's barefoot children wandered over. From the gray mud huts with the untidy heads that stood within a decorated mud wall, chickens, and dogs with their skin stretched like parchment over their bones, followed the piccanins down to the track. The flushed and perspiring west cast a reflection, faint, without heat, upon the station, upon the tin shed marked "Goods," upon the walled kraal, upon the gray tin house of the stationmaster and upon the sand, that lapped all around, from sky to sky, cast little rhythmical cups of shadow, so that the sand became the sea, and closed over the children's black feet softly and without imprint.

---

chalet roof: a steeply sloped roof
serge: a woolen fabric
parchment: a paperlike material made from animal skin
piccanins: derogatory slang term for black children
kraal: a small enclosure or pen for livestock

The stationmaster's wife sat behind the mesh of her veranda. Above her head the hunk of a sheep's carcass moved slightly, dangling in a current of air.

They waited.

The train called out, along the sky; but there was no answer; and the cry hung on: I'm coming…I'm coming…

The engine flared out now, big, whisking a dwindling body behind it; the track flared out to let it in.

Creaking, jerking, jostling, gasping, the train filled the station.

Here, let me see that one—the young woman curved her body further out of the corridor window. Missus? smiled the old boy, looking at the creatures he held in his hand. From a piece of string on his gray finger hung a tiny woven basket; he lifted it, questioning. No, no, she urged, leaning down toward him, across the height of the train, toward the man in the piece of old rug; that one, that one, her hand commanded. It was a lion, carved out of soft dry wood that looked like spongecake; heraldic, black and white, with impressionistic detail burnt in. The old man held it up to her still smiling, not from the heart, but at the customer. Between its Vandyke teeth, in the mouth opened in an endless roar too terrible to be heard, it had a black tongue. Look, said the young husband, if you don't mind! And round the neck of the thing, a piece of fur (rat? rabbit? meerkat?); a real mane, majestic, telling you somehow that the artist had delight in the lion.

All up and down the length of the train in the dust the artists sprang, walking bent, like performing animals, the better to exhibit the fantasy held toward the faces on the train. Bucks, startled and stiff, staring with round black and white eyes. More lions, standing erect, grappling with strange, thin, elongated warriors who clutched

---

veranda: porch
dwindling: diminishing; becoming smaller
heraldic: signifying rank or social importance
impressionistic: designed to give the impression of reflected light
Vandyke: having a series of V-shaped points (like a Vandyke, an old form of broad
    collar with a pointed or scalloped edge)
grappling: struggling; wrestling or fighting

spears and showed no fear in their slits of eyes. How much, they asked from the train, how much?

Give me penny, said the little ones with nothing to sell. The dogs went and sat, quite still, under the dining car, where the train breathed out the smell of meat cooking with onion.

A man passed beneath the arch of reaching arms meeting gray-black and white in the exchange of money for the staring wooden eyes, the stiff wooden legs sticking up in the air; went along under the voices and the bargaining, interrogating the wheels. Past the dogs; glancing up at the dining car where he could stare at the faces, behind glass, drinking beer, two by two, on either side of a uniform railway vase with its pale dead flower. Right to the end, to the guard's van, where the stationmaster's children had just collected their mother's two loaves of bread; to the engine itself, where the stationmaster and the driver stood talking against the steaming complaint of the resting beast.

The man called out to them, something loud and joking. They turned to laugh, in a twirl of steam. The two children careered over the sand, clutching the bread, and burst through the iron gate and up the path through the garden in which nothing grew.

Passengers drew themselves in at the corridor windows and turned into compartments to fetch money, to call someone to look. Those sitting inside looked up: suddenly different, caged faces, boxed in, cut off, after the contact of outside. There was an orange a piccanin would like.... What about that chocolate? It wasn't very nice....

A young girl had collected a handful of the hard kind, that no one liked, out of the chocolate box, and was throwing them to the dogs, over at the dining car. But the hens darted in, and swallowed the chocolates, incredibly quick and accurate, before they had even dropped in the dust, and the dogs, a little bewildered, looked up with their brown eyes, not expecting anything.

—No, leave it, said the girl, don't take it....

---

interrogating: inspecting
careered: moved headfirst and at high speed
bewildered: confused

Too expensive, too much, she shook her head and raised her voice to the old boy, giving up the lion. He held it up where she had handed it to him. No, she said, shaking her head. Three-and-six? insisted her husband, loudly. Yes baas! laughed the boy. *Three-and-six?*—the young man was incredulous. Oh leave it—she said. The young man stopped. Don't you want it? he said, keeping his face closed to the boy. No, never mind, she said, leave it. The old native kept his head on one side, looking at them sideways, holding the lion. Three-and-six, he murmured, as old people repeat things to themselves.

The young woman drew her head in. She went into the coupé and sat down. Out of the window, on the other side, there was nothing; sand and bush; a thorn tree. Back through the open doorway, past the figure of her husband in the corridor, there was the station, the voices, wooden animals waving, running feet. Her eye followed the funny little valance of scrolled wood that outlined the chalet roof of the station; she thought of the lion and smiled. That bit of fur round the neck. But the wooden buck, the hippos, the elephants, the baskets that already bulked out of their brown paper under the seat and on the luggage rack! How will they look at home? Where will you put them? What will they mean away from the places you found them? Away from the unreality of the last few weeks? The man outside. But he is not part of the unreality; he is for good now. Odd…somewhere there was an idea that he, that living with him, was part of the holiday, the strange places.

Outside, a bell rang. The stationmaster was leaning against the end of the train, green flag rolled in readiness. A few men who had got down to stretch their legs sprang on to the train, clinging to the observation platforms, or perhaps merely standing on the iron step, holding the rail; but on the train, safe from the one dusty platform, the one tin house, the empty sand.

There was a grunt. The train jerked. Through the glass the beer drinkers looked out, as if they could not see beyond it. Behind the

---

three-and-six: three shillings and sixpence; a small amount of money
baas: boss
incredulous: shocked
coupé: train car
valance: a decorative framework

flyscreen, the stationmaster's wife sat facing back at them beneath the darkening hunk of meat.

There was a shout. The flag dropped out. Joints not yet coordinated, the segmented body of the train heaved and bumped back against itself. It began to move; slowly the scrolled chalet moved past it, the yells of the natives, running alongside, jetted up into the air, fell back at different levels. Staring wooden faces waved drunkenly, there, then gone, questioning for the last time at the windows. Here, one-and-six baas!—As one automatically opens a hand to catch a thrown ball, a man fumbled wildly down his pocket, brought up the shilling and sixpence and threw them out; the old native, gasping, his skinny toes splaying the sand, flung the lion.

The piccanins were waving, the dogs stood, tails uncertain, watching the train go: past the mud huts, where a woman turned to look, up from the smoke of the fire, her hand pausing on her hip.

The stationmaster went slowly in under the chalet.

The old native stood, breath blowing out the skin between his ribs, feet tense, balanced in the sand, smiling and shaking his head. In his opened palm, held in the attitude of receiving, was the retrieved shilling and sixpence.

The blind end of the train was being pulled helplessly out of the station.

The young man swung in from the corridor, breathless. He was shaking his head with laughter and triumph. Here! he said. And waggled the lion at her. One-and-six!

What? she said.

He laughed. I was arguing with him for fun, bargaining— when the train had pulled out already, he came tearing after.... One-and-six baas! So there's your lion.

She was holding it away from her, the head with the open jaws, the pointed teeth, the black tongue, the wonderful ruff of fur facing her. She was looking at it with an expression of not seeing, of seeing something different. Her face was drawn up, wryly, like the face of a discomforted child. Her mouth lifted nervously at the

---

flyscreen: protective netting or screen that prevents insects from entering

corner. Very slowly, cautious, she lifted her finger and touched the mane, where it was joined to the wood.

But how could you, she said. He was shocked by the dismay of her face.

Good heavens, he said, what's the matter?

If you wanted the thing, she said, her voice rising and breaking with the shrill impotence of anger, why didn't you buy it in the first place? If you wanted it, why didn't you pay for it? Why didn't you take it decently, when he offered it? Why did you have to wait for him to run after the train with it, and give him one-and-six? One-and six!

She was pushing it at him, trying to force him to take it. He stood astonished, his hands hanging at his sides.

But you wanted it! You liked it so much?

—It's a beautiful piece of work, she said fiercely, as if to protect it from him.

You liked it so much! You said yourself it was too expensive—

Oh *you*—she said, hopeless and furious. *You*.... She threw the lion onto the seat.

He stood looking at her.

She sat down again in the corner and, her face slumped in her hand, stared out of the window. Everything was turning round inside her. One-and-six. One-and-six. One-and-six for the wood and the carving and the sinews of the legs and the switch of the tail. The mouth open like that and the teeth. The black tongue, rolling, like a wave. The mane round the neck. To give one-and-six for that. The heat of shame mounted through her legs and body and sounded in her ears like the sound of sand pouring. Pouring, pouring. She sat there, sick. A weariness, a tastelessness, the discovery of a void made her hands slacken their grip, atrophy emptily, as if the hour was not worth their grasp. She was feeling like this again. She had thought it was something to do with singleness, with being alone and belonging too much to oneself.

---

dismay: disapproval
shrill: high-pitched
impotence: powerlessness
slacken: loosen
atrophy: grow weak

She sat there not wanting to move or speak, or to look at anything, even; so that the mood should be associated with nothing, no object, word or sight that might recur and so recall the feeling again…. Smuts blew in grittily, settled on her hands. Her back remained at exactly the same angle, turned against the young man sitting with his hands drooping between his sprawled legs, and the lion, fallen on its side in the corner.

The train had cast the station like a skin. It called out to the sky, I'm coming, I'm coming; and again, there was no answer.

---

smuts: cinders; particles of soot or coal
cast: shed

POISON

Roald Dahl

Though best known as a writer of books for children, including James and the Giant Peach *and* Charlie and the Chocolate Factory, *the British writer Roald Dahl (1916–1990) also wrote stories for adults. "Poison" is set in India during the time of British colonial rule.*

It must have been around midnight when I drove home, and as I approached the gates of the bungalow I switched off the headlamps of the car so the beam wouldn't swing in through the window of the side bedroom and wake Harry Pope. But I needn't have bothered. Coming up the drive I noticed his light was still on, so he was awake anyway— unless perhaps he'd dropped off while reading.

I parked the car and went up the five steps to the balcony, counting each step carefully in the dark so I wouldn't take an extra one which wasn't there when I got to the top. I crossed the balcony, pushed through the screen doors into the house itself, and switched on the light in the hall. I went across to the door of Harry's room, opened it quietly, and looked in.

He was lying on the bed and I could see he was awake. But he didn't move. He didn't even turn his head towards me, but I heard him say, "Timber, Timber, come here." He spoke slowly, whispering each word carefully, separately, and I pushed the door right open and started to go quickly across the room.

"Stop. Wait a moment, Timber." I could hardly hear what he was saying. He seemed to be straining enormously to get the words out.

"What's the matter, Harry?"

"Sshhh!" he whispered. "Sshhh! For God's sake, don't make a noise. Take your shoes off before you come nearer. *Please* do as I say, Timber."

---

bungalow: a small house

The way he was speaking reminded me of George Barling after he got shot in the stomach, when he stood leaning against a crate containing a spare airplane engine, holding both hands on his stomach and saying things about the German pilot in just the same hoarse, straining half whisper Harry was using now.

"Quickly, Timber, but take your shoes off first."

I couldn't understand about taking off the shoes, but I figured that if he was as ill as he sounded I'd better humor him, so I bent down and removed the shoes and left them in the middle of the floor. Then I went over to his bed.

"Don't touch the bed! For God's sake, don't touch the bed!" He was still speaking like he'd been shot in the stomach, and I could see him lying there on his back with a single sheet covering three-quarters of his body. He was wearing a pair of pajamas with blue, brown, and white stripes, and he was sweating terribly. It was a hot night, and I was sweating a little myself, but not like Harry. His whole face was wet, and the pillow around his head was sodden with moisture. It looked like a bad go of malaria to me.

"What is it, Harry?"

"A krait," he said.

"A *krait!* Oh, my God! Where'd it bite you? How long ago?"

"Shut up," he whispered.

"Listen, Harry," I said, and I leaned forward and touched his shoulder. "We've got to be quick. Come on now, quickly, tell me where it bit you." He was lying there very still and tense as though he was holding on to himself hard because of sharp pain.

"I haven't been bitten," he whispered. "Not yet. It's on my stomach. Lying there asleep."

I took a quick pace backward; I couldn't help it, and I stared at his stomach or rather at the sheet that covered it. The sheet was rumpled in several places and it was impossible to tell if there was anything underneath.

"You don't really mean there's a krait lying on your stomach now?"

---

hoarse: rough; scratchy
sodden: soaked
malaria: a disease transmitted through the bite of a kind of mosquito
krait: a type of poisonous snake found in India and Southeast Asia

"I swear it."

"How did it get there?" I shouldn't have asked the question because it was easy to see he wasn't fooling. I should have told him to keep quiet.

"I was reading," Harry said, and he spoke very slowly, taking each word in turn and speaking it carefully so as not to move the muscles of his stomach. "Lying on my back reading and I felt something on my chest, behind the book. Sort of tickling. Then out of the corner of my eye saw this little krait sliding over my pajamas. Small, about ten inches. Knew I mustn't move. Couldn't have anyway. Lay there watching it. Thought it would go over top of the sheet." Harry paused and was silent for a few moments. His eyes looked down along his body towards the place where the sheet covered his stomach, and I could see he was watching to make sure his whispering wasn't disturbing the thing that lay there.

"There was a fold in the sheet," he said, speaking more slowly than ever now and so softly I had to lean close to hear him. "See it, it's still there. It went under that. I could feel it through my pajamas, moving on my stomach. Then it stopped moving and now it's lying there in the warmth. Probably asleep. I've been waiting for you." He raised his eyes and looked at me.

"How long ago?"

"Hours," he whispered. "Hours and bloody hours and hours. I can't keep still much longer. I've been wanting to cough."

There was not much doubt about the truth of Harry's story. As a matter of fact it wasn't a surprising thing for a krait to do. They hang around people's houses, and they go for the warm places. The surprising thing was that Harry hadn't been bitten. The bite is quite deadly except sometimes when you catch it at once, and they kill a fair number of people each year in Bengal, mostly in the villages.

"All right, Harry," I said, and now I was whispering too. "Don't move and don't talk anymore unless you have to. You know it won't bite unless it's frightened. We'll fix it in no time."

I went softly out of the room in my stocking feet and fetched a small sharp knife from the kitchen. I put it in my trouser pocket, ready to use instantly in case something went wrong while we were

---

Bengal: a region that is today a part of both India and Bangladesh

163

still thinking out a plan. If Harry coughed or moved or did something to frighten the krait and got bitten, I was going to be ready to cut the bitten place and try to suck the venom out. I came back to the bedroom and Harry was still lying there very quiet and sweating all over his face. His eyes followed me as I moved across the room to his bed, and I could see he was wondering what I'd been up to. I stood beside him, trying to think of the best thing to do.

"Harry," I said, and now when I spoke I put my mouth almost on his ear so I wouldn't have to raise my voice above the softest whisper, "I think the best thing to do is for me to draw the sheet back very, very gently. Then we could have a look first. I think I could do that without disturbing it."

"Don't be a fool." There was no expression in his voice. He spoke each word too slowly, too carefully, and too softly for that. The expression was in the eyes and around the corners of the mouth.

"Why not?"

"The light would frighten him. It's dark under there now."

"Then how about whipping the sheet back quick and brushing it off before it has time to strike?"

"Why don't you get a doctor?" Harry said. The way he looked at me told me I should have thought of that myself in the first place.

"A doctor. Of course. That's it. I'll get Ganderbai."

I tiptoed out to the hall, looked up Ganderbai's number in the book, lifted the phone, and told the operator to hurry.

"Doctor Ganderbai," I said. "This is Timber Woods."

"Hello, Mr. Woods. You not in bed yet?"

"Look, could you come round at once? And bring serum—for a krait bite."

"Who's been bitten?" The question came so sharply it was like a small explosion in my ear.

"No one. No one yet. But Harry Pope's in bed and he's got one lying on his stomach—asleep under the sheet on his stomach."

For about three seconds there was silence on the line. Then speaking slowly, not like an explosion now but slowly, precisely,

---

serum: antidote; medicine meant to treat a person bitten by a venomous snake

Ganderbai said, "Tell him to keep quite still. He is not to move or to talk. Do you understand?"

"Of course."

"I'll come at once!" He rang off and I went back to the bedroom. Harry's eyes watched me as I walked across to his bed.

"Ganderbai's coming. He said for you to lie still."

"What does he think I'm doing!"

"Look, Harry, he said no talking. Absolutely no talking. Either of us."

"Why don't you shut up then?" When he said this, one side of his mouth started twitching with rapid little downward movements that continued for a while after he finished speaking. I took out my handkerchief and very gently I wiped the sweat off his face and neck, and I could feel the slight twitching of the muscle—the one he used for smiling—as my fingers passed over it with the handkerchief.

I slipped out to the kitchen, got some ice from the ice-box, rolled it up in a napkin, and began to crush it small. That business of the mouth, I didn't like that. Or the way he talked, either. I carried the ice pack back to the bedroom and laid it across Harry's forehead.

"Keep you cool."

He screwed up his eyes and drew breath sharply through his teeth. "Take it away," he whispered. "Make me cough." His smiling-muscle began to twitch again.

The beam of a headlamp shone through the window as Ganderbai's car swung around to the front of the bungalow. I went out to meet him, holding the ice pack with both hands.

"How is it?" Ganderbai asked, but he didn't stop to talk; he walked on past me across the balcony and through the screen doors into the hall. "Where is he? Which room?"

He put his bag down on a chair in the hall and followed me into Harry's room. He was wearing soft-soled bedroom slippers and he walked across the floor noiselessly, delicately, like a careful cat. Harry watched him out of the sides of his eyes. When Ganderbai reached the bed be looked down at Harry and smiled, confident and reassuring, nodding his head to tell Harry it was

---

rang off: hung up

165

a simple matter and he was not to worry but just to leave it to Doctor Ganderbai. Then he turned and went back to the hall and I followed him.

"First thing is to try to get some serum into him," he said, and he opened his bag and started to make preparations. "Intravenously. But I must do it neatly. Don't want to make him flinch."

We went into the kitchen and he sterilized a needle. He had a hypodermic syringe in one hand and a small bottle in the other, and he stuck the needle through the rubber top of the bottle and began drawing a pale yellow liquid up into the syringe by pulling out the plunger. Then he handed the syringe to me.

"Hold that till I ask for it."

He picked up the bag and together we returned to the room. Harry's eyes were bright now and wide open. Ganderbai bent over Harry and very cautiously, like a man handling sixteenth-century lace, he rolled up the pajama sleeve to the elbow without moving the arm. I noticed he stood well away from the bed.

He whispered, "I'm going to give you an injection. Serum. Just a prick but try not to move. Don't tighten your stomach muscles. Let them go limp."

Harry looked at the syringe.

Ganderbai took a piece of red rubber tubing from his bag and slid one end under and up and around Harry's biceps; then he tied the tubing tight with a knot. He sponged a small area of the bare forearm with alcohol, handed the swab to me, and took the syringe from my hand. He held it up to the light, squinting at the calibrations, squirting out some of the yellow fluid. I stood still beside him, watching. Harry was watching too and sweating all over his face so it shone like it was smeared thick with face cream melting on his skin and running down onto the pillow.

I could see the blue vein on the inside of Harry's forearm, swollen now because of the tourniquet, and then I saw the needle

---

intravenously: through the veins; via injection

hypodermic syringe: a medical tool for injecting fluids into the body

biceps: a muscle in the upper arm, above the elbow

calibrations: measurements

tourniquet: a bandage or other object (in this case, rubber tubing) wrapped tightly
    around an arm or leg to stop blood flow

above the vein, Ganderbai holding the syringe almost flat against the arm, sliding the needle in sideways through the skin into the blue vein, sliding it slowly but so firmly it went in smooth as into cheese. Harry looked at the ceiling and closed his eyes and opened them again but he didn't move.

When it was finished Ganderbai leaned forward putting his mouth close to Harry's ear. "Now you'll be all right even if you are bitten. But don't move. Please don't move. I'll be back in a moment."

He picked up his bag and went out to the hall and I followed.

"Is he safe now?" I asked.

"No."

"How safe is he?"

The little Indian doctor stood there in the hall rubbing his lower lip.

"It must give some protection, mustn't it?" I asked.

He turned away and walked to the screen doors that led onto the veranda. I thought he was going through them, but he stopped this side of the doors and stood looking out into the night.

"Isn't the serum very good?" I asked.

"Unfortunately not," he answered without turning round. "It might save him. It might not. I am trying to think of something else to do."

"Shall we draw the sheet back quick and brush it off before it has time to strike?"

"Never! We are not entitled to take a risk." He spoke sharply and his voice was pitched a little higher than usual.

"We can't very well leave him lying there," I said. "He's getting nervous."

"Please! Please!" he said, turning round, holding both hands up in the air. "Not so fast, please. This is not a matter to rush into bald-headed." He wiped his forehead with his handkerchief and stood there, frowning, nibbling his lip.

---

veranda: porch or patio
baldheaded: unprepared

"You see," he said at last. "There is a way to do this. You know what we must do—we must administer an anesthetic to the creature where it lies."

It was a splendid idea.

"It is not safe," he continued, "because a snake is coldblooded and anesthetic does not work so well or so quick with such animals, but it is better than any other thing to do. We could use ether…chloroform…" He was speaking slowly and trying to think the thing out while he talked.

"Which shall we use?"

"Chloroform," he said suddenly. "Ordinary chloroform. That is best. Now quick!" He took my arm and pulled me toward the balcony. "Drive to my house! By the time you get there I will have waked up my boy on the telephone and he will show you my poisons cupboard. Here is the key of the cupboard. Take a bottle of chloroform. It has an orange label and the name is printed on it. I'll stay here in case anything happens. Be quick now, hurry! No, no, you don't need your shoes!"

I drove fast and in about fifteen minutes I was back with the bottle of chloroform. Ganderbai came out of Harry's room and met me in the hall. "You got it?" he said. "Good, good. I've just been telling him what we are going to do. But now we must hurry. It is not easy for him in there like that all this time. I am afraid he might move."

He went back to the bedroom and I followed, carrying the bottle carefully with both hands. Harry was lying on the bed in precisely the same position as before with the sweat pouring down his cheeks. His face was white and wet. He turned his eyes toward me, and I smiled at him and nodded confidently. He continued to look at me. I raised my thumb, giving him the okay signal. He closed his eyes. Ganderbai was squatted down by the bed, and on the floor beside him was the hollow rubber tube that he had previously used as a tourniquet, and he'd got a small paper funnel fitted into one end of the tube.

---

ether…chloroform: chemicals once commonly used as anesthetics during medical
    procedures

He began to pull a little piece of the sheet out from under the mattress. He was working directly in line with Harry's stomach, about eighteen inches from it, and I watched his fingers as they tugged gently at the edge of the sheet. He worked so slowly it was almost impossible to discern any movement either in his fingers or in the sheet that was being pulled.

Finally he succeeded in making an opening under the sheet and he took the rubber tube and inserted one end of it in the opening so that it would slide under the sheet along the mattress toward Harry's body. I do not know how long it took him to slide that tube in a few inches. It may have been twenty minutes, it may have been forty. I never once saw the tube move. I knew it was going in because the visible part of it grew gradually shorter, but I doubted that the krait could have felt even the faintest vibration. Ganderbai himself was sweating now, large pearls of sweat standing out all over his forehead and along his upper lip. But his hands were steady, and I noticed that his eyes were watching, not the tube in his hands, but the area of crumpled sheet above Harry's stomach.

Without looking up, he held out a hand to me for the chloroform. I twisted out the ground-glass stopper and put the bottle right into his hand, not letting go till I was sure he had a good hold on it. Then he jerked his head for me to come closer, and he whispered, "Tell him I'm going to soak the mattress and that it will be very cold under his body. He must be ready for that and he must not move. Tell him now."

I bent over Harry and passed on the message.

"Why doesn't he get on with it?" Harry said.

"He's going to now, Harry. But it'll feel very cold, so be ready for it."

"Oh, get on!" For the first time he raised his voice, and Ganderbai glanced up sharply, watched him for a few seconds, then went back to his business.

Ganderbai poured a few drops of chloroform into the paper funnel and waited while it ran down the tube. Then he poured some more. Then he waited again, and the heavy, sickening smell of chloroform spread out over the room, bringing with it faint

---

discern: notice

169

unpleasant memories of white-coated nurses and white surgeons standing in a white room around a long white table. Ganderbai was pouring steadily now, and I could see the heavy vapor of the chloroform swirling slowly like smoke above the paper funnel. He paused, held the bottle up to the light, poured one more funnelful, and handed the bottle back to me. Slowly he drew out the rubber tube from under the sheet; then he stood up.

The strain of inserting the tube and pouring the chloroform must have been great, and I recollect that when Ganderbai turned and whispered to me, his voice was small and tired, "We'll give it fifteen minutes just to be safe."

I leaned over to tell Harry. "We're going to give it fifteen minutes, just to be safe. But it's probably done for already."

"Then why don't you look and see!" Again he spoke loudly and Ganderbai sprang round, his small brown face suddenly very angry. He had almost pure black eyes and he stared at Harry and Harry's smiling-muscle started to twitch. I took my handkerchief and wiped his wet face, trying to stroke his forehead a little for comfort as I did so.

Then we stood and waited beside the bed, Ganderbai watching Harry's face all the time in a curious intense manner. The little Indian was concentrating all his willpower on keeping Harry quiet. He never once took his eyes from the patient and although he made no sound, he seemed somehow to be shouting at him all the time, saying: Now listen, you've got to listen, you're not going to go spoiling this now, d'you hear me; and Harry lay there twitching his mouth, sweating, closing his eyes, opening them, looking at me, at the sheet, at the ceiling, at me again, but never at Ganderbai. Yet somehow Ganderbai was holding him. The smell of chloroform was oppressive and it made me feel sick, but I couldn't leave the room now. I had the feeling someone was blowing up a huge balloon and I could see it was going to burst, but I couldn't look away.

At length Ganderbai turned and nodded and I knew he was ready to proceed. "You go over to the other side of the bed," he said. "We will each take one side of the sheet and draw it back together, but very slowly please, and very quietly."

---

oppressive: overpowering

170

"Keep still now, Harry," I said, and I went around to the other side of the bed and took hold of the sheet. Ganderbai stood opposite me, and together we began to draw back the sheet, lifting it up clear of Harry's body, taking it back very slowly, both of us standing well away but at the same time bending forward, trying to peer underneath it. The smell of chloroform was awful. I remember trying to hold my breath, and when I couldn't do that any longer, I tried to breathe shallow so the stuff wouldn't get into my lungs.

The whole of Harry's chest was visible now, or rather the striped pajama top which covered it, and then I saw the white cord of his pajama trousers, neatly tied in a bow. A little farther and I saw a button, a mother-of-pearl button, and that was something I had never had on my pajamas, a fly button, let alone a mother-of-pearl one. This Harry, I thought, he is very refined. It is odd how one sometimes has frivolous thoughts at exciting moments, and I distinctly remember thinking about Harry being very refined when I saw that button.

Apart from the button there was nothing on his stomach.

We pulled the sheet back faster then, and when we had uncovered his legs and feet we let the sheet drop over the end of the bed on to the floor.

"Don't move," Ganderbai said, "don't move, Mr. Pope"; and he began to peer around along the side of Harry's body and under his legs.

"We must be careful," he said. "It may be anywhere. It could be up the leg of his pajamas."

When Ganderbai said this, Harry quickly raised his head from the pillow and looked down at his legs. It was the first time he had moved. Then suddenly he jumped up, stood on his bed, and shook his legs one after the other violently in the air. At that moment we both thought he had been bitten, and Ganderbai was already reaching down into his bag for a scalpel and a tourniquet when Harry ceased his caperings and stood still and looked at the mattress he was standing on and shouted, "It's not there!"

---

refined: sophisticated; proper
frivolous: lighthearted; silly
scalpel: a surgeon's knife
caperings: jumps; leaps

Ganderbai straightened up and for a moment he too looked at the mattress; then he looked up at Harry. Harry was all right. He hadn't been bitten and now he wasn't going to get bitten and he wasn't going to be killed and everything was fine. But that didn't seem to make anyone feel any better.

"Mr. Pope, you are of course quite sure you saw it in the first place?" There was a note of sarcasm in Ganderbai's voice that he would never have employed in ordinary circumstances. "You don't think you might possibly have been dreaming, do you, Mr. Pope?" The way Ganderbai was looking at Harry, I realized that the sarcasm was not seriously intended. He was only easing up a bit after the strain.

Harry stood on his bed in his striped pajamas, glaring at Ganderbai, and the color began to spread out over his cheeks.

"Are you telling me I'm a liar?" he shouted.

Ganderbai remained absolutely still, watching Harry. Harry took a pace forward on the bed and there was a shining look in his eyes.

"Why, you dirty little sewer rat!"

"Shut up, Harry!" I said.

"You dirty black—"

"Harry!" I called. "Shut up, Harry!" It was terrible, the things he was saying.

Ganderbai went out of the room as though neither of us was there, and I followed him and put my arm around his shoulder as he walked across the hall and out on to the balcony.

"Don't you listen to Harry," I said. "This thing's made him so he doesn't know what he's saying."

We went down the steps from the balcony to the drive and across the drive in the darkness to where his old Morris car was parked. He opened the door and got in.

"You did a wonderful job," I said. "Thank you so very much for coming."

"All he needs is a good holiday," he said quietly, without looking at me; then he started the engine and drove off.

---

holiday: vacation

THROUGH THE TUNNEL

Doris Lessing

A well-known campaigner against nuclear arms and against racial inequality in Africa, Doris Lessing was born to British parents in 1919 in what is now Iran. She was raised primarily in southern Rhodesia, now Zimbabwe, in south-central Africa. In 2007 she was awarded the Nobel Prize in Literature. "Through the Tunnel" was first published in 1955.

Going to the shore on the first morning of the vacation, the young English boy stopped at a turning of the path and looked down at a wild and rocky bay, and then over the crowded beach he knew so well from other years. His mother walked on in front of him, carrying a bright striped bag in one hand. Her other arm, swinging loose, was very white in the sun. The boy watched that white, naked arm, and turned his eyes, which had a frown behind them, toward the bay and back again to his mother. When she felt he was not with her, she swung around. "Oh, there you are, Jerry!" she said. She looked impatient, then smiled. "Why, darling, would you rather not come with me? Would you rather—" She frowned, conscientiously worrying over what amusements he might secretly be longing for, which she had been too busy or too careless to imagine. He was very familiar with that anxious, apologetic smile. Contrition sent him running after her. And yet, as he ran, he looked back over his shoulder at the wild bay; and all morning, as he played on the safe beach, he was thinking of it.

Next morning, when it was time for the routine of swimming and sunbathing, his mother said, "Are you tired of the usual beach, Jerry? Would you like to go somewhere else?"

---

conscientiously: with great care; with concern to do what is right
contrition: sorrow; regret

"Oh, no!" he said quickly, smiling at her out of that unfailing impulse of contrition—a sort of chivalry. Yet, walking down the path with her, he blurted out, "I'd like to go and have a look at those rocks down there."

She gave the idea her attention. It was a wild-looking place, and there was no one there; but she said, "Of course, Jerry. When you've had enough, come to the big beach. Or just go straight back to the villa, if you like." She walked away, that bare arm, now slightly reddened from yesterday's sun, swinging. And he almost ran after her again, feeling it unbearable that she should go by herself, but he did not.

She was thinking, Of course he's old enough to be safe without me. Have I been keeping him too close? He mustn't feel he ought to be with me. I must be careful.

He was an only child, eleven years old. She was a widow. She was determined to be neither possessive nor lacking in devotion. She went worrying off to her beach.

As for Jerry, once he saw that his mother had gained her beach, he began the steep descent to the bay. From where he was, high up among red-brown rocks, it was a scoop of moving bluish green fringed with white. As he went lower, he saw that it spread among small promontories and inlets of rough, sharp rock, and the crisping, lapping surface showed stains of purple and darker blue. Finally, as he ran sliding and scraping down the last few yards, he saw an edge of white surf and the shallow, luminous movement of water over white sand, and, beyond that, a solid, heavy blue.

He ran straight into the water and began swimming. He was a good swimmer. He went out fast over the gleaming sand, over a middle region where rocks lay like discolored monsters under the surface, and then he was in the real sea—a warm sea where irregular cold currents from the deep water shocked his limbs.

When he was so far out that he could look back not only on the little bay but past the promontory that was between it and the big beach, he floated on the buoyant surface and looked for his mother.

chivalry: gallantry; courtesy; noble, selfless behavior
promontories: high points of land or rock projecting into the sea
luminous: bright
buoyant: capable of keeping objects afloat

There she was, a speck of yellow under an umbrella that looked like a slice of orange peel. He swam back to shore, relieved at being sure she was there, but all at once very lonely.

On the edge of a small cape that marked the side of the bay away from the promontory was a loose scatter of rocks. Above them, some boys were stripping off their clothes. They came running, naked, down to the rocks. The English boy swam toward them, but kept his distance at a stone's throw. They were of that coast; all of them were burned smooth dark brown and speaking a language he did not understand. To be with them, of them, was a craving that filled his whole body. He swam a little closer; they turned and watched him with narrowed, alert dark eyes. Then one smiled and waved. It was enough. In a minute, he had swum in and was on the rocks beside them, smiling with a desperate, nervous supplication. They shouted cheerful greetings at him; and then, as he preserved his nervous, uncomprehending smile, they understood that he was a foreigner strayed from his own beach, and they proceeded to forget him. But he was happy. He was with them.

They began diving again and again from a high point into a well of blue sea between rough, pointed rocks. After they had dived and come up, they swam around, hauled themselves up, and waited their turn to dive again. They were big boys—men, to Jerry. He dived, and they watched him; and when he swam around to take his place, they made way for him. He felt he was accepted and he dived again, carefully, proud of himself.

Soon the biggest of the boys poised himself, shot down into the water, and did not come up. The others stood about, watching. Jerry, after waiting for the sleek brown head to appear, let out a yell of warning; they looked at him idly and turned their eyes back toward the water. After a long time, the boy came up on the other side of a big dark rock, letting the air out of his lungs in a sputtering gasp and a shout of triumph. Immediately the rest of them dived in. One moment, the morning seemed full of chattering boys; the next, the air and the surface of the water were empty. But

---

cape: peninsula; strip of land projecting into a body of water
supplication: plea
poised: readied
idly: casually

through the heavy blue, dark shapes could be seen moving and groping.

Jerry dived, shot past the school of underwater swimmers, saw a black wall of rock looming at him, touched it, and bobbed up at once to the surface, where the wall was a low barrier he could see across. There was no one visible; under him, in the water, the dim shapes of the swimmers had disappeared. Then one, and then another of the boys came up on the far side of the barrier of rock, and he understood that they had swum through some gap or hole in it. He plunged down again. He could see nothing through the stinging salt water but the blank rock. When he came up the boys were all on the diving rock, preparing to attempt the feat again. And now, in a panic of failure, he yelled up, in English, "Look at me! Look!" and he began splashing and kicking in the water like a foolish dog.

They looked down gravely, frowning. He knew the frown. At moments of failure, when he clowned to claim his mother's attention, it was with just this grave, embarrassed inspection that she rewarded him. Through his hot shame, feeling the pleading grin on his face like a scar that he could never remove, he looked up at the group of big brown boys on the rock and shouted, *"Bonjour! Merci! Au revoir! Monsieur, monsieur!"* while he hooked his fingers round his ears and waggled them.

Water surged into his mouth; he choked, sank, came up. The rock, lately weighted with boys, seemed to rear up out of the water as their weight was removed. They were flying down past him, now, into the water; the air was full of falling bodies. Then the rock was empty in the hot sunlight. He counted one, two, three....

At fifty, he was terrified. They must all be drowning beneath him, in the watery caves of the rock! At a hundred, he stared around him at the empty hillside, wondering if he should yell for help. He counted faster, faster, to hurry them up, to bring them to the surface quickly, to drown them quickly—anything rather than the terror of counting on and on into the blue emptiness of the morning. And then, at a hundred and sixty, the water beyond the

---

Bonjour! Merci! Au revoir! Monsieur, monsieur!: French words meaning "Hello! Thank you! Goodbye! Sir, sir!"

rock was full of boys blowing like brown whales. They swam back to the shore without a look at him.

He climbed back to the diving rock and sat down, feeling the hot roughness of it under his thighs. The boys were gathering up their bits of clothing and running off along the shore to another promontory. They were leaving to get away from him. He cried openly, fists in his eyes. There was no one to see him, and he cried himself out.

It seemed to him that a long time had passed, and he swam out to where he could see his mother. Yes, she was still there, a yellow spot under an orange umbrella. He swam back to the big rock, climbed up, and dived into the blue pool among the fanged and angry boulders. Down he went, until he touched the wall of rock again. But the salt was so painful in his eyes that he could not see.

He came to the surface, swam to shore and went back to the villa to wait for his mother. Soon she walked slowly up the path, swinging her striped bag, the flushed, naked arm dangling beside her. "I want some swimming goggles," he panted, defiant and beseeching.

She gave him a patient, inquisitive look as she said casually, "Well, of course, darling."

But now, now, now! He must have them this minute, and no other time. He nagged and pestered until she went with him to a shop. As soon as she had bought the goggles, he grabbed them from her hand as if she were going to claim them for herself, and was off, running down the steep path to the bay.

Jerry swam out to the big barrier rock, adjusted the goggles, and dived. The impact of the water broke the rubber-enclosed vacuum, and the goggles came loose. He understood that he must swim down to the base of the rock from the surface of the water. He fixed the goggles tight and firm, filled his lungs, and floated, face down, on the water. Now, he could see. It was as if he had eyes of a different kind—fish eyes that showed everything clear and delicate and wavering in the bright water.

---

beseeching: pleading
inquisitive: questioning
wavering: flickering

Under him, six or seven feet down, was a floor of perfectly clean, shining white sand, rippled firm and hard by the tides. Two grayish shapes steered there, like long, rounded pieces of wood or slate. They were fish. He saw them nose toward each other, poise motionless, make a dart forward, swerve off, and come around again. It was like a water dance. A few inches above them the water sparkled as if sequins were dropping through it. Fish again—myriads of minute fish, the length of his fingernail, were drifting through the water, and in a moment he could feel the innumerable tiny touches of them against his limbs. It was like swimming in flaked silver. The great rock the big boys had swum through rose sheer out of the white sand—black, tufted lightly with greenish weed. He could see no gap in it. He swam down to its base.

Again and again he rose, took a big chestful of air, and went down. Again and again he groped over the surface of the rock, feeling it, almost hugging it in the desperate need to find the entrance. And then, once, while he was clinging to the black wall, his knees came up and he shot his feet out forward and they met no obstacle. He had found the hole.

He gained the surface, clambered about the stones that littered the barrier rock until he found a big one, and, with this in his arms, let himself down over the side of the rock. He dropped, with the weight, straight to the sandy floor. Clinging tight to the anchor of stone, he lay on his side and looked in under the dark shelf at the place where his feet had gone. He could see the hole. It was an irregular, dark gap; but he could not see deep into it. He let go of his anchor, clung with his hands to the edge of the hole, and tried to push himself in.

He got his head in, found his shoulders jammed, moved them in sidewise, and was inside as far as his waist. He could see nothing ahead. Something soft and clammy touched his mouth; he saw a dark frond moving against the grayish rock, and panic filled him.

---

poise: to attain a balanced or suspended state
myriads: large numbers
minute: small
innumerable: countless
clambered: climbed clumsily
clammy: slimy

He thought of octopuses, of clinging weed. He pushed himself out backward and caught a glimpse, as he retreated, of a harmless tentacle of seaweed drifting in mouth of the tunnel. But it was enough. He reached the sunlight, swam to shore, and lay on the diving rock. He looked down into the blue well of water. He knew he must find his way through that cave, or hole, or tunnel, and out the other side.

First, he thought, he must learn to control his breathing. He let himself down into the water with another big stone in his arms, so that he could lie effortlessly on the bottom of the sea. He counted. One, two, three. He counted steadily. He could hear the movement of blood in his chest. Fifty-one, fifty-two.... His chest was hurting. He let go of the rock and went up into the air. He saw that the sun was low. He rushed to the villa and found his mother at her supper. She said only "Did you enjoy yourself?" and he said "Yes."

All night the boy dreamed of the water-filled cave in the rock, and as soon as breakfast was over he went to the bay.

That night, his nose bled badly. For hours he had been under water, learning to hold his breath, and now he felt weak and dizzy. His mother said, "I shouldn't overdo things, darling, if I were you."

That day and the next, Jerry exercised his lungs as if everything, the whole of his life, all that he would become, depended upon it. Again his nose bled at night, and his mother insisted on his coming with her the next day. It was a torment to him to waste a day of his careful self-training, but he stayed with her on that other beach, which now seemed a place for small children, a place where his mother might lie safe in the sun. It was not his beach.

He did not ask for permission, on the following day, to go to his beach. He went, before his mother could consider the complicated rights and wrongs of the matter. A day's rest, he discovered, had improved his count by ten. The big boys had made the passage while he counted a hundred and sixty. He had been counting fast, in his fright. Probably now, if he tried, he could get through the long tunnel, but he was not going to try yet. A curious, most unchildlike persistence, a controlled impatience, made him wait. In the meantime, he lay underwater on the white sand, littered now by stones he had brought down from the upper air, and studied the entrance to the tunnel. He knew every jut and corner of it, as far as it was possible to see. It was as if he already felt its sharpness about his shoulders.

He sat by the clock in the villa, when his mother was not near, and checked his time. He was incredulous and then proud to find he could hold his breath without strain for two minutes: The words "two minutes," authorized by the clock, brought close the adventure that was so necessary to him.

In another four days, his mother said casually one morning, they must go home. On the day before they left, he would do it. He would do it if it killed him, he said defiantly to himself. But two days before they were to leave—a day of triumph when he increased his count by fifteen—his nose bled so badly that he turned dizzy and had to lie limply over the big rock like a bit of seaweed, watching the thick red blood flow on to the rock and trickle slowly down to the sea. He was frightened. Supposing he turned dizzy in the tunnel? Supposing he died there, trapped? Supposing—his head went around, in the hot sun, and he almost gave up. He thought he would return to the house and lie down, and next summer, perhaps, when he had another year's growth in him—*then* he would go through the hole.

But even after he had made the decision, or thought he had, he found himself sitting up on the rock and looking down into the water; and he knew that now, this moment, when his nose had only just stopped bleeding, when his head was still sore and throbbing— this was the moment when he would try. If he did not do it now, he never would. He was trembling with fear that he would not go; and he was trembling with horror at that long, long tunnel under the rock, under the sea. Even in the open sunlight, the barrier rock seemed very wide and very heavy; tons of rock pressed down on where he would go. If he died there, he would lie until one day— perhaps not before next year—those big boys would swim into it and find it blocked.

He put on his goggles, fitted them tight, tested the vacuum. His hands were shaking. Then he chose the biggest stone he could carry and slipped over the edge of the rock until half of him was in the

---

incredulous: unbelieving
authorized: confirmed

cool, enclosing water and half in the hot sun. He looked up once at the empty sky, filled his lungs once, twice, and then sank fast to the bottom with the stone. He let it go and began to count. He took the edges of the hole in his hands and drew himself into it, wriggling his shoulders in sidewise as he remembered he must, kicking himself along with his feet.

Soon he was clear inside. He was in a small rockbound hole filled with yellowish-gray water. The water was pushing him up against the roof. The roof was sharp and pained his back. He pulled himself along with his hands—fast, fast—and used his legs as levers. His head knocked against something; a sharp pain dizzied him. Fifty, fifty-one, fifty-two…. He was without light, and the water seemed to press upon him with the weight of rock. Seventy-one, seventy-two…. There was no strain on his lungs. He felt like an inflated balloon, his lungs were so light and easy, but his head was pulsing.

He was being continually pressed against the sharp roof, which felt slimy as well as sharp. Again he thought of octopuses, and wondered if the tunnel might be filled with weed that could tangle him. He gave himself a panicky, convulsive kick forward, ducked his head, and swam. His feet and hands moved freely, as if in open water. The hole must have widened out. He thought he must be swimming fast, and he was frightened of banging his head if the tunnel narrowed.

A hundred, a hundred and one…. The water paled. Victory filled him. His lungs were beginning to hurt. A few more strokes and he would be out. He was counting wildly; he said a hundred and fifteen, and then, a long time later, a hundred and fifteen again. The water was a clear jewel-green all around him. Then he saw, above his head, a crack running up through the rock. Sunlight was falling through it, showing the clean, dark rock of the tunnel, a single mussel shell, and darkness ahead.

He was at the end of what he could do. He looked up at the crack as if it were filled with air and not water, as if he could put his mouth to it to draw in air. A hundred and fifteen, he heard himself say inside his head—but he had said that long ago. He

---

convulsive: jerky; spasmodic

must go on into the blackness ahead, or he would drown. His head was swelling, his lungs cracking. A hundred and fifteen, a hundred and fifteen pounded through his head, and he feebly clutched at rocks in the dark, pulling himself forward, leaving the brief space of sunlit water behind. He felt he was dying. He was no longer quite conscious. He struggled on in the darkness between lapses into unconsciousness. An immense, swelling pain filled his head, and then the darkness cracked with an explosion of green light. His hands, groping forward, met nothing; and his feet, kicking back, propelled him out into the open sea.

He drifted to the surface, his face turned up to the air. He was gasping like a fish. He felt he would sink now and drown; he could not swim the few feet back to the rock. Then he was clutching it and pulling himself up on to it. He lay face down, gasping. He could see nothing but a red-veined, clotted dark. His eyes must have burst, he thought; they were full of blood. He tore off his goggles and a gout of blood went into the sea. His nose was bleeding, and the blood had filled the goggles.

He scooped up handfuls of water from the cool, salty sea, to splash on his face, and did not know whether it was blood or salt water he tasted. After a time, his heart quieted, his eyes cleared, and he sat up. He could see the local boys diving and playing half a mile away. He did not want them. He wanted nothing but to get back home and lie down.

In a short while, Jerry swam to shore and climbed slowly up the path to the villa. He flung himself on his bed and slept, waking at the sound of feet on the path outside. His mother was coming back. He rushed to the bathroom, thinking she must not see his face with bloodstains, or tearstains, on it. He came out of the bathroom and met her as she walked into the villa, smiling, her eyes lighting up.

"Have a nice morning?" she asked, laying her hand on his warm brown shoulder.

"Oh, yes, thank you," he said.

"You look a bit pale." And then, sharp and anxious, "How did you bang your head?"

"Oh, just banged it," he told her.

---

gout: clot

She looked at him closely. He was strained; his eyes were glazed-looking. She was worried. And then she said to herself, Oh, don't fuss! Nothing can happen. He can swim like a fish.

They sat down to lunch together.

"Mummy," he said, "I can stay under water for two minutes— three minutes, at least." It came bursting out of him.

"Can you, darling?" she said. "Well, I shouldn't overdo it. I don't think you ought to swim any more today."

She was ready for a battle of wills, but he gave in at once. It was no longer of the least importance to go the bay.

Shooting an Elephant

George Orwell

George Orwell (1903–1950) was the pseudonym of Eric Arthur Blair, a twentieth-century English author best known for his novels Animal Farm *and* Nineteen Eighty-Four. *The autobiographical essay that follows is based in part on Orwell's experiences as a colonial police officer in Burma in the 1920s.*

In Moulmein, in Lower Burma, I was hated by large numbers of people—the only time in my life that I have been important enough for this to happen to me. I was sub-divisional police officer of the town, and in an aimless, petty kind of way anti-European feeling was very bitter. No one had the guts to raise a riot, but if a European woman went through the bazaars alone somebody would probably spit betel juice over her dress. As a police officer I was an obvious target and was baited whenever it seemed safe to do so. When a nimble Burman tripped me up on the football field and the referee (another Burman) looked the other way, the crowd yelled with hideous laughter. This happened more than once. In the end the sneering yellow faces of young men that met me everywhere, the insults hooted after me when I was at a safe distance, got badly on my nerves. The young Buddhist priests were the worst of all. There were several thousands of them in the town and none of them seemed to have anything to do except stand on street corners and jeer at Europeans.

Burma: now Myanmar, a country in Southeast Asia that borders the Bay of Bengal
bazaars: shopping areas or marketplaces
betel juice: saliva resulting from chewing the leaves of the betel plant
baited: lured into a fight

All this was perplexing and upsetting. For at that time I had already made up my mind that imperialism was an evil thing and the sooner I chucked up my job and got out of it the better. Theoretically—and secretly, of course—I was all for the Burmese and all against their oppressors, the British. As for the job I was doing, I hated it more bitterly than I can perhaps make clear. In a job like that you see the dirty work of Empire at close quarters. The wretched prisoners huddling in the stinking cages of the lock-ups, the grey, cowed faces of the long-term convicts, the scarred buttocks of the men who had been flogged with bamboos—all these oppressed me with an intolerable sense of guilt. But I could get nothing into perspective. I was young and ill-educated and I had had to think out my problems in the utter silence that is imposed on every Englishman in the East. I did not even know that the British Empire is dying, still less did I know that it is a great deal better than the younger empires that are going to supplant it. All I knew was that I was stuck between my hatred of the empire I served and my rage against the evil-spirited little beasts who tried to make my job impossible. With one part of my mind I thought of the British Raj as an unbreakable tyranny, as something clamped down, *in saecula saeculorum*, upon the will of prostrate peoples; with another part I thought that the greatest joy in the world would be to drive a bayonet into a Buddhist priest's guts. Feelings like these are the normal by-products of imperialism; ask any Anglo-Indian official, if you can catch him off duty.

One day something happened which in a roundabout way was enlightening. It was a tiny incident in itself, but it gave me a better glimpse than I had had before of the real nature of imperialism—the real motives for which despotic governments act. Early one

---

perplexing: confusing
imperialism: empire building; the policy or action by which one country controls
    another country or territory
cowed: frightened and intimidated
flogged: beaten
imposed: forced
British Raj: British rule in India and Southeast Asia
in saecula saeculorum: Latin phrase meaning "forever and ever"
prostrate: lying face downward
despotic: tyrannical

morning the sub-inspector at a police station the other end of the town rang me up on the phone and said that an elephant was ravaging the bazaar. Would I please come and do something about it? I did not know what I could do, but I wanted to see what was happening and I got on to a pony and started out. I took my rifle, an old .44 Winchester and much too small to kill an elephant, but I thought the noise might be useful *in terrorem*. Various Burmans stopped me on the way and told me about the elephant's doings. It was not, of course, a wild elephant, but a tame one which had gone "must." It had been chained up as tame elephants always are when their attack of "must" is due, but on the previous night it had broken its chain and escaped. Its mahout, the only person who could manage it when it was in that state, had set out in pursuit, but he had taken the wrong direction and was now twelve hours' journey away, and in the morning the elephant had suddenly reappeared in the town. The Burmese population had no weapons and were quite helpless against it. It had already destroyed some-body's bamboo hut, killed a cow and raided some fruit-stalls and devoured the stock; also it had met the municipal rubbish van, and, when the driver jumped out and took to his heels, had turned the van over and inflicted violence upon it.

The Burmese sub-inspector and some Indian constables were waiting for me in the quarter where the elephant had been seen. It was a very poor quarter, a labyrinth of squalid bamboo huts, thatched with palm-leaf, winding all over a steep hillside. I remember that it was a cloudy stuffy morning at the beginning of the rains. We began questioning the people as to where the elephant had gone, and, as usual, failed to get any definite informa-tion. That is invariably the case in the East; a story always sounds clear enough at a distance, but the nearer you get to the scene of events the vaguer it becomes. Some of the people said that the elephant had gone in one direction, some said that he had gone in another, some professed not even to have heard of any elephant. I

---

in terrorem: Latin phrase meaning "in fear" or "to frighten"
must: a period of highly aggressive behavior triggered by mating instincts
mahout: an elephant keeper or trainer
labyrinth: a maze; a place full of complex, interconnected passageways
squalid: filthy

had almost made up my mind that the whole story was a pack of lies, when we heard yells a little distance away. There was a loud, scandalised cry of "Go away, child! Go away this instant!" and an old woman with a switch in her hand came round the corner of a hut, violently shooing away a crowd of naked children. Some more women followed, clicking their tongues and exclaiming; evidently there was something there that the children ought not to have seen. I rounded the hut and saw a man's dead body sprawling in the mud. He was an Indian, a black Dravidian coolie, almost naked, and he could not have been dead many minutes. The people said that the elephant had come suddenly upon him round the corner of the hut, caught him with its trunk, put its foot on his back and ground him into the earth. This was the rainy season and the ground was soft, and his face had scored a trench a foot deep and a couple of yards long. He was lying on his belly with arms crucified and head sharply twisted to one side. His face was coated with mud, the eyes wide open, the teeth bared and grinning with an expression of unendurable agony. (Never tell me, by the way, that the dead look peaceful. Most of the corpses I have seen looked devilish.) The friction of the great beast's foot had stripped the skin from his back as neatly as one skins a rabbit. As soon as I saw the dead man I sent an orderly to a friend's house nearby to borrow an elephant rifle. I had already sent back the pony, not wanting it to go mad with fright and throw me if it smelled the elephant.

The orderly came back in a few minutes with a rifle and five cartridges, and meanwhile some Burmans had arrived and told us that the elephant was in the paddy fields below, only a few hundred yards away. As I started forward practically the whole population of the quarter flocked out of their houses and followed me. They had seen the rifle and were all shouting excitedly that I was going to shoot the elephant. They had not shown much interest in the elephant when he was merely ravaging their homes, but it was different now that he was going to be shot. It was a bit of fun to them, as it would be to an English crowd; besides, they wanted the

---

Dravidian: a person from southern India
coolie: a laborer; the term is now considered to be offensive
paddy fields: rice fields

187

meat. It made me vaguely uneasy. I had no intention of shooting the elephant—I had merely sent for the rifle to defend myself if necessary—and it is always unnerving to have a crowd following you. I marched down the hill, looking and feeling a fool, with the rifle over my shoulder and an ever-growing army of people jostling at my heels. At the bottom, when you got away from the huts, there was a metalled road and beyond that a miry waste of paddy fields a thousand yards across, not yet ploughed but soggy from the first rains and dotted with coarse grass. The elephant was standing eighty yards from the road, his left side towards us. He took not the slightest notice of the crowd's approach. He was tearing up bunches of grass, beating them against his knees to clean them and stuffing them into his mouth.

I had halted on the road. As soon as I saw the elephant I knew with perfect certainty that I ought not to shoot him. It is a serious matter to shoot a working elephant—it is comparable to destroying a huge and costly piece of machinery—and obviously one ought not to do it if it can possibly be avoided. And at that distance, peacefully eating, the elephant looked no more dangerous than a cow. I thought then and I think now that his attack of "must" was already passing off; in which case he would merely wander harmlessly about until the mahout came back and caught him. Moreover, I did not in the least want to shoot him. I decided that I would watch him for a little while to make sure that he did not turn savage again, and then go home.

But at that moment I glanced round at the crowd that had followed me. It was an immense crowd, two thousand at the least and growing every minute. It blocked the road for a long distance on either side. I looked at the sea of yellow faces above the garish clothes—faces all happy and excited over this bit of fun, all certain that the elephant was going to be shot. They were watching me as they would watch a conjuror about to perform a trick. They did not

---

jostling: pushing and shoving
metalled: paved
miry: boggy; marshy
ploughed: variant spelling of "plowed"
garish: tastelessly bright; gaudy
conjuror: magician

like me, but with the magical rifle in my hands I was momentarily worth watching. And suddenly I realised that I should have to shoot the elephant after all. The people expected it of me and I had got to do it; I could feel their two thousand wills pressing me forward, irresistibly. And it was at this moment, as I stood there with the rifle in my hands, that I first grasped the hollowness, the futility of the white man's dominion in the East. Here was I, the white man with his gun, standing in front of the unarmed native crowd — seemingly the leading actor of the piece; but in reality I was only an absurd puppet pushed to and fro by the will of those yellow faces behind. I perceived in this moment that when the white man turns tyrant it is his own freedom that he destroys. He becomes a sort of hollow, posing dummy, the conventionalised figure of a sahib. For it is the condition of his rule that he shall spend his life in trying to impress the "natives" and so in every crisis he has got to do what the "natives" expect of him. He wears a mask, and his face grows to fit it. I had got to shoot the elephant. I had committed myself to doing it when I sent for the rifle. A sahib has got to act like a sahib; he has got to appear resolute, to know his own mind and do definite things. To come all that way, rifle in hand, with two thousand people marching at my heels, and then to trail feebly away, having done nothing — no, that was impossible. The crowd would laugh at me. And my whole life, every white man's life in the East, was one long struggle not to be laughed at.

But I did not want to shoot the elephant. I watched him beating his bunch of grass against his knees, with that preoccupied grand-motherly air that elephants have. It seemed to me that it would be murder to shoot him. At that age I was not squeamish about killing animals, but I had never shot an elephant and never wanted to. (Somehow it always seems worse to kill a *large* animal.) Besides, there was the beast's owner to be considered. Alive, the elephant was worth at least a hundred pounds; dead, he would only be worth the value of his tusks — five pounds, possibly. But I had got

---

futility: pointlessness

dominion: rule

sahib: a title meaning "master," which was once used to show respect to Europeans
    in India and other parts of Southeast Asia

resolute: firm; determined

to act quickly. I turned to some experienced-looking Burmans who had been there when we arrived, and asked them how the elephant had been behaving. They all said the same thing: he took no notice of you if you left him alone, but he might charge if you went too close to him.

It was perfectly clear to me what I ought to do. I ought to walk up to within, say, twenty-five yards of the elephant and test his behaviour. If he charged I could shoot, if he took no notice of me it would be safe to leave him until the mahout came back. But also I knew that I was going to do no such thing. I was a poor shot with a rifle and the ground was soft mud into which one would sink at every step. If the elephant charged and I missed him, I should have about as much chance as a toad under a steam-roller. But even then I was not thinking particularly of my own skin, only the watchful yellow faces behind. For at that moment, with the crowd watching me, I was not afraid in the ordinary sense, as I would have been if I had been alone. A white man mustn't be frightened in front of "natives"; and so, in general, he isn't frightened. The sole thought in my mind was that if anything went wrong those two thousand Burmans would see me pursued, caught, trampled on and reduced to a grinning corpse like that Indian up the hill. And if that happened it was quite probable that some of them would laugh. That would never do. There was only one alternative. I shoved the cartridges into the magazine and lay down on the road to get a better aim.

The crowd grew very still, and a deep, low, happy sigh, as of people who see the theatre curtain go up at last, breathed from innumerable throats. They were going to have their bit of fun after all. The rifle was a beautiful German thing with cross-hair sights. I did not then know that in shooting an elephant one should shoot to cut an imaginary bar running from ear-hole to ear-hole. I ought therefore, as the elephant was sideways on, to have aimed straight at his ear-hole; actually I aimed several inches in front of this, thinking the brain would be further forward.

When I pulled the trigger I did not hear the bang or feel the kick—one never does when a shot goes home—but I heard the devilish roar of glee that went up from the crowd. In that instant, in too short a time, one would have thought, even for the bullet to get there, a mysterious, terrible change had come over the elephant. He neither stirred nor fell, but every line of his body had altered. He looked suddenly stricken, shrunken, immensely old, as though the frightful impact of the bullet had paralysed him without knocking him down. At last, after what seemed a long time—it might have been five seconds, I dare say—he sagged flabbily to his knees. His mouth slobbered. An enormous senility seemed to have settled upon him. One could have imagined him thousands of years old. I fired again into the same spot. At the second shot he did not collapse but climbed with desperate slowness to his feet and stood weakly upright, with legs sagging and head drooping. I fired a third time. That was the shot that did for him. You could see the agony of it jolt his whole body and knock the last remnant of strength from his legs. But in falling he seemed for a moment to rise, for as his hind legs collapsed beneath him he seemed to tower upwards like a huge rock toppling, his trunk reaching skyward like a tree. He trumpeted, for the first and only time. And then down he came, his belly towards me, with a crash that seemed to shake the ground even where I lay.

I got up. The Burmans were already racing past me across the mud. It was obvious that the elephant would never rise again, but he was not dead. He was breathing very rhythmically with long rattling gasps, his great mound of a side painfully rising and falling. His mouth was wide open—I could see far down into caverns of pale pink throat. I waited a long time for him to die, but his breathing did not weaken. Finally I fired my two remaining shots into the spot where I thought his heart must be. The thick blood welled out of him like red velvet, but still he did not die. His body did not even jerk when the shots hit him, the tortured breathing continued without a pause. He was dying, very slowly and in great agony, but in some world remote from me where not even a bullet could damage him further. I felt that I had got to put an end to that dreadful noise. It seemed dreadful to see the great beast lying there, powerless to move and yet powerless to die, and not even to be able to finish him. I sent back for my small rifle and poured shot after shot into his heart and down his throat. They

---

senility: state of extreme infirmity due to old age

seemed to make no impression. The tortured gasps continued as steadily as the ticking of a clock.

In the end I could not stand it any longer and went away. I heard later that it took him half an hour to die. Burmans were arriving with dahs and baskets even before I left, and I was told they had stripped his body almost to the bones by the afternoon.

Afterwards, of course, there were endless discussions about the shooting of the elephant. The owner was furious, but he was only an Indian and could do nothing. Besides, legally I had done the right thing, for a mad elephant has to be killed, like a mad dog, if its owner fails to control it. Among the Europeans opinion was divided. The older men said I was right, the younger men said it was a damn shame to shoot an elephant for killing a coolie, because an elephant was worth more than any damn Coringhee coolie. And afterwards I was very glad that the coolie had been killed; it put me legally in the right and it gave me a sufficient pretext for shooting the elephant. I often wondered whether any of the others grasped that I had done it solely to avoid looking a fool.

---

dahs: knives
Coringhee: a person from Coringa, India
pretext: a made-up reason; an excuse

192

INDEX OF AUTHORS AND TITLES

Acknowledgments

"Eveline" from DUBLINERS by James Joyce. Copyright 1916 by B.W. Heubsch. Definitive text Copyright © 1967 by the Estate of James Joyce. Used by permission of Viking Penguin, a division of Penguin Group (USA) Inc.

"Four seasons fill the measure of the year." Reprinted by permission of the publisher from JOHN KEATS COMPLETE POEMS, edited by Jack Stillinger, pp. 176–177, Cambridge, Mass.: The Belknap Press of Harvard University Press. Copyright © 1978, 1982 by the President and Fellows of Harvard College.

"Poison" from SOMEONE LIKE YOU by Roald Dahl. Copyright 1950. Used by permission of David Higham Associates, Ltd.

"Pulling Up the Baobab Tree" from "Childhood" and "The Lion's Awakening" from SUNDIATA: AN EPIC OF OLD MALI by D. T. Niane, translated by G.D. Pickett. Copyright 1960 by Presence Africaine. English translation copyright 1965 by Longman Group, Ltd. (Pearson Education Limited).

"A Red Red Rose" from SONGS & POEMS by Robert Burns, edited by J. Kinley (2004), Oxford University Press.

"The Rocking-Horse Winner." Copyright 1933 by the Estate of D.H. Lawrence, renewed © 1961 by Angelo Ravagli and C.M. Weekley, Executors of the Estate of Frieda Lawrence, from COMPLETE SHORT STORIES OF D.H. LAWRENCE by D.H. Lawrence. Used by permission of Viking Penguin, a division of Penguin Group (USA) Inc.

"Shooting an Elephant" from SHOOTING AN ELEPHANT AND OTHER ESSAYS by George Orwell. Copyright 1950 by Sonia Brownell Orwell and renewed 1978 by Sonia Pitt-Rivers. Reprinted by permission of Houghton Mifflin Harcourt Publishing Company.

"Through the Tunnel" from THE HABIT OF LOVING by Doris Lessing. Copyright © 1955 by Doris Lessing. Originally appeared in The New Yorker. Reprinted by permission of HarperCollins Publishers.

"The Train from Rhodesia." Reprinted by the permission of Russell & Volkening as agents for the author. Copyright © 1950 by Nadine Gordimer, renewed in 1978 by Nadine Gordimer.

While every care has been taken to trace and acknowledge copyright, the editors tender their apologies for any accidental infringement when copyright has proven untraceable. They would be pleased to include the appropriate acknowledgment in any subsequent edition of this publication.